Forgotten Books

The Diall of Princes

By

Antonio De Guevara N. Colvilewm

Published by Forgotten Books 2012

Originally Published 1919

PIBN 1000234097

THE DIALL OF PRINCES

THE SCHOLAR'S LIBRARY

THE DIALL
OF PRINCES:

BY DON ANTHONY OF GUEVARA

TRANSLATED BY
SIR THOMAS NORTH

BEING SELECT PASSAGES
NOW SET FORTH WITH AN INTRO-
DUCTION AND A BIBLIOGRAPHY
BY

K.   E

MCM   LONDON   XIX
PHILIP ALLAN & CO.

THE TABLE

		PAGE
THE INTRODUCTION		ix
BIBLIOGRAPHY		xlii

NORTH'S 'THE DIALL OF PRINCES'

DEDICATION		3
THE TABLE OF 'THE DIALL OF PRINCES'	. .	7
BOOK I. cap. xliii.	Of Princes and Sages .	27
BOOK II. 1. cap. v.	The Story of Sinoris and Camma . .	33
2. cap. xiv.-xvii.	The Colloquy of Marcus and Faustine concerning the Key of the Study	42
BOOK III. 1. cap. iii.-v.	The Villain of the Danube	97
2. cap. xiii.-xvi.	Against Wars of Conquest . . .	124
3. cap. xix.-xxii.	A Letter to Claudius and Claudinus, which had many years and little discretion . .	168
4. cap. xlviii.	On Mortality and the Fear of Death . .	204
BOOK IV. cap. vii.-viii.	Manners for Courtiers .	219

APPENDIX A.	Extracts from Guevara and Berthault	257
APPENDIX B.	Extract from Berners' *Golden Boke* .	259
APPENDIX C.	Extract from Bryan's *Dispraise of the Life of a Courtier* . . .	260
APPENDIX D.	Extract from Fenton's *Golden Epistles*	262

The Diall of Princes.

own

ı his

ame

hich

ıous

ɜlox

ʒues

ıub-

‧‧ _ _ _ _ _ _ _ _ _ .lred

CORRIGENDA.

——

Page xiii., line 24, *for* 1527, *read* 1528.
,,   xv., line 6, *for* 1534, *read* 1535
,,   ,, line 8, *for* 1535, *read* 1536
,,   xxi., line 27, *for* 1557, *read* 1577.
,,   xxii., line 13, *for* Calvaria, *read* Calvarie.
,,   xxxv., line 8, *delete* all.
,,   ,, line 18, *for* borrowing, *read* borrowings.

years after its first appearance it was constantly in the printers' hands. ' Scarce any book except the Bible,' wrote Merik Casaubon, ' has been so much translated or so frequently printed.' But the neglect of the succeeding three centuries has been as complete as was that early triumph. Even at the opening of the eighteenth century we find Bayle writing :

' He should have been contented with the glory which his haranguing gained him : for by his attempting to write books, he made himself ridiculous to good judges. His inflated and figurative style, crowded with antitheses, is not the greatest

THE INTRODUCTION

§ 1

FEW literary reputations have been so blown upon as Don Anthony of Guevara's. In his own day there was no more famous name than his in the whole republic of letters, which Western Europe then truly was. His famous 'Libro aureo,' or its enlarged version 'Lo relox de principes,' was translated into all tongues (there was even an Armenian version published at Venice in 1738), and for a hundred years after its first appearance it was constantly in the printers' hands. 'Scarce any book except the Bible,' wrote Merik Casaubon, ' has been so much translated or so frequently printed.' But the neglect of the succeeding three centuries has been as complete as was that early triumph. Even at the opening of the eighteenth century we find Bayle writing :

' He should have been contented with the glory which his haranguing gained him : for by his attempting to write books, he made himself ridiculous to good judges. His inflated and figurative style, crowded with antitheses, is not the greatest defect in his compositions. He was led to this way of writing by a bad taste, a false idea he had formed to himself of eloquence; but this was nothing when compared to his romantic way of writing history.'

In justice to both Guevara and Bayle it should be remembered that the latter was born into an age which achieved the highest fame in a style of art the furthest removed from the 'romantic,' and that even Shakespeare was looked on as an 'intoxicated barbarian.' But to-day, when the pendulum might have been expected to have swung back, it may be doubted if even in Spain any but a few professed scholars ever read a word of all those writings of Guevara in which the Elizabethans so greatly delighted; and his name is recorded in the histories of our own literature only because of the eminence of two of his translators, Lord Berners and Sir Thomas North, and of the influence which he is supposed, with doubtful justice, to have exercised over the prose literature of that age.

§ 2

The most famous Sir Anthony of Guevara, 'Preacher, Chronicler and Councillour to the Emperour Charles the fifth,' was a noble

Castilian, born, probably in the year 1480,[1] at Santander. His father was Don Beltran de Guevara ; his mother before her marriage was Elvira de Norona y Calderon, a lady-in-waiting to Isabella of Castile. He was sent, at the age of twelve, to be educated with Queen Isabella's pages, and with Prince John, by one Pedro Martir de Angleria. From that time onwards Don Anthony was always more or less a 'courtier,' though he eventually became a priest and entered the Franciscan order. In 1521 he was appointed Preacher and Chronicler to the Emperor Charles the Fifth, and in the following year accompanied him to England. But already he may have had personal intercourse with one prominent Englishman, for John Bourchier, Lord Berners, had come on a mission to the Spanish court in 1518, in the lifetime of Maximilian. In 1523 he was given a seat on the Council of the Inquisition of Toledo, and in 1527 we hear of him being recommended by Charles

---

[1] On February 12, 1524, he wrote to Don Alonso Espinel : 'De mi, senor, os se dezir que he hecho recuento con mis anos y hallo por mis memoriales que he los quarenta y quatro cumplidos' (quoted by M. de Burgos : Introd. to 'Menosprecio de Corte,' Madrid, 1915). In another letter (quoted by the same writer), dated October 8, 1525, he says he has been thirty-eight years at the Imperial court. But he says in the Prologo to the 'Menosprecio' that he was brought to the court at the age of twelve, by which reckoning he was born in 1475.

to the Pope for the Bishopric of Guadix, in
Granada, but he does not seem to have been
installed in that see till 1529, the year of
the publication of his famous *Relox*. Even so
he did not relinquish his courtly duties, and
in 1535 he embarked with Charles at Bar-
celona on his expedition to Tunis, whence
he returned in the Emperor's train to Italy.
At this time he probably made the acquaintance of another Englishman of literary fame,
Sir Thomas Elyot, author of *The Governour*,
who was also with Charles on this occasion.
In 1539 he was translated to Mondonedo, in
Galicia, and this year also saw the publication of his *Aviso de Privados, Menosprecio de
Corte, Arte de Marear*, and the first part of
Epistolas Familiares. In 1542 appeared the
second part of this last, and also *Misterios del
Monte Calvario*, and *Oratorio de religiosos y
exercicio de virtuosos*. He died at Mondonedo
April 3, 1545, and was buried in the Cathedral
there. But in 1552 his body was removed
to the Church of San Francisco in Valladolid,
which church, with its convent and its tombs,
disappeared in 1837.

§ 3

It was in 1518, according to his own account
of the matter, that Guevara began to put

together into a volume the ' Life and Letters of Marcus Aurelius,' alleging them to be translated from a Greek work he had found at Florence. In the existence of this Greek work, however, no scholar appears ever to have believed. Some time after (so he informs us in the *Menosprecio*), he having lent this MS. to the Emperor, it was surreptitiously copied and printed, first at Seville and then in Portugal. In a later letter (*Ep. Fam.*, fol. 220) he amplifies this tale. He there says :

' As concerning that which you write of Marcus Aurelius, the case standeth thus : that I translated and presented it unto Cæsar not at all finished, the which Laxao did steal from the Emperor, and the Queene from Laxao, and Tumbas from the Queene, and the Ladie Aldonsa from Tumbas, and your lordship from the Ladie Aldonsa in such wise that my sweat is ended in your theftes.'

This pirated version (if the Bishop is to be believed) was the famous *Libro aureo*, or Golden Boke of Marcus Aurelius, which Lord Berners translated. A copy of the Seville edition, dated 1527, is said to be in the Biblioteca Nacional at Madrid : of the Portuguese edition no trace is to be found. In 1529 Guevara himself put forth the fuller version known as *Libro de Emperador Marco Aurelio cõ relox de principes*, which North long afterwards translated as *The Diall of Princes, with the famous booke of Marcus Aurelius.* The inversion of the two parts of the title is found in the French version, *Lorloge des Princes, auquel est contenu le livre d'or de Marc Aurele Empereur*, and the Latin version is similarly styled *Horologium Principum.*

Guevara's statement that the book was translated from the Greek, even if there had been any Greek original, would need qualifying, for he elsewhere admits that he knew no Greek but used others' translations into Latin or Castilian. The colophon of Berners' version indicates the course supposed to have been followed in this case.

§ 4

Berners' translation, the *Golden Boke,* was undertaken by the veteran soldier penman at the close of his life, when he was residing at Calais (of which town and the marches thereof he was governor), and at the instigation of his nephew Sir Francis Bryan, himself calling for later mention in connection with a cognate matter. Berners is best known by his great translation of Froissart (1523-5), and he had also translated *The History of*

Arthur of Lytell Brytaine and *The Boke of Duke Huon of Bordeaux*. He finished the *Golden Boke* only a little while before his death in 1533, and it was published posthumously. The earliest known edition is that represented by a copy, dated 1534, in the Bodleian Library, which also has a copy dated 1535. The earliest copy in the British Museum is one dated 1539, which accounts for the vagaries of the bibliographers in this matter.

The colophon of the first edition runs :

Thus endeth the volume of Marke Aurelie emperour otherwyse called the golden boke, translated out of Frenche into englysshe by John Bourchier Knyghte lorde Berners, deputie generall of the kynges towne of Caleys and marches of the same, at the instant desyre of his neuewe syr Francis Bryan knyght, ended at Caleys the tenth day of Marche, in the yere of the reygne of our Soueraygne lorde kynge Henrye the viii the xxiii

LONDINI IN ÆDIBUS THO-
MÆ BERTHELETI RE-
GII IMPRESSORIS
CVM PRIVILEGIO A RE-
GE INDVLTO.

Later editions (1553 onwards) read xxiiii for xxiii, but there is no reason for assuming the correctness of the alteration. The tenth day of March in the twenty-third year of Henry VIII. would be 1532. Berners died in 1533.

The last paragraph of the book proper begins :

' Thus endeth the golden boke of the eloquent Marc Aurelie emperour . . . Certainly as great prayse as oughte to be gyven to the author is to be gyven to the translators that have laboriously reduced this treatise oute of Greke into Latin, and out of Castilian into french and out of french into Englishe. Written in high and swete styles.'

This mode of translation through the French is that employed not by Berners only but by every subsequent English translator from Guevara's writings. The reference to the ' high and swete styles ' is interesting as showing wherein lay the principal attraction of Guevara for Berners and Bryan. But Guevara himself had claimed merit on the same ground, for in the Prologue to the *Diall* we read :

' Let all men judge what I have suffered in drawing it out of Greeke into latin, out of the latin in the vulgar, and out of a plaine vulgar into a sweete and pleasaint stile. For that banket is not counted sumptuous, unless there be both pleasaint meats and savory sauces. To call sentences to minde, to place the wordes, to examine languages, to conect sillables : what sweat I have suffered . . . let other prove, if me they wil not credit.'

In the *Golden Boke* (*Libro aureo*) there is very little, if anything, that is not to be found in the *Diall* (*Relox*), but the arrangement of the common element is quite different. The *Golden Boke* contains only forty-eight chapters of the history of Marcus Aurelius, together with nineteen letters. The later work, omitting the fourth book, contains 145 chapters, divided into three books, together with a number of additional letters, eighteen in the original, twelve in North's version. Several of the letters of the *Libro aureo* are relegated to this latter body. The most famous episodes in the later book are however already embodied in the earlier, for example that of Faustina and the study key, that of the villain of the Danube, and the letters on War to Cornelius, and to Claudius and Claudine, printed in this volume.

Hallam (*Literature of the Middle Ages*) claims that the *Golden Boke* always, in all languages, remained the more popular book, and though Hallam was not very exactly informed concerning the various editions, and even Dr. West, on whose authority he

b

inserted a long note in his second edition, was not accurate in his bibliographic facts, yet a glance at the list of editions of the two books on pp. xlii-xliii will show that there is a good deal to support this view. Certainly the *Diall* did not wholly supersede the *Golden Boke.*

§ 5

If Berners is chiefly linked on men's tongues with Froissart, so North, Guevara's other great translator, is linked with Plutarch. Thomas North was the second son of the first Lord North, but neither his birth nor his death can be precisely dated. The years 1535 and 1601 are those generally accepted for these events, and as Guevara furnished Berners with a last task for his declining years, so to North he furnished a first one for his ' green, unknowing youth.' He is said to have studied at Cambridge, and he entered Lincoln's Inn in 1557, the year of the publication of *The Diall of Princes.* He would thus, if the date assigned to his birth be correct, have been not more than twenty-two when he made his version. In 1568 he added to the original three books a fourth, which is a translation of Guevara's *Aviso de Privados,*

first published in 1539.   In 1570 he published
' The Moral Philosophie : drawne out of the
auncient writers.   A work first compiled in
the Indian tongue, and afterwards reduced
into divers other languages : and now lastly
Englished out of the Italian by Thomas
North.'   In 1579 appeared his great title to
fame, his version, through the French of
Amyot, of Plutarch's *Lives*.

The Diall of Princes is, as has been said, a
version—the first in the language—of the full,
authentic text of Guevara's book.   Like
Berners, and setting himself an example to
be so profitably followed when he came to
handle Plutarch, North translated by the
aid of a French intermediary.[1]   The version
called *L'orloge des Princes* by Rene Berthault was first published in 1540.   Berthault's *Livre d'ore de Marc Aurele*, published
nine years earlier, had already been used by
Berners.   But none of Berthault's editions,
nor of de Herberay's, a later translator,
appear to have contained the *Aviso de Privados*.   For this North might have used the
version entitled *Le Favori de Court*, by J. de
Rochemore, of which there is a Lyons edition,
dated 1556, and an Antwerp one, dated 1557.

[1] See note on p. xli.

This first appears in *The Diall,* as its fourth
book, in the 1568 edition.   As the name suggests, it is a treatise rather on the satellites of
princes than on princes themselves, though
it bears indirectly on the theme of the earlier
work as well.

This addition by North to his original work
is an indication of the popularity of his book,
and others now began to feed the appetite
which North had whetted.

§ 6

Hitherto only one piece besides the *Libro
aureo* had been Englished.   That was *Menosprecio de Corte y alabanza de aldea,* translated
by Lord Berners' nephew and adviser, Sir
Francis Bryan(t), a poet of note in his own
day, though all his work has perished save
his unidentified contributions to Tottel's
Miscellany, his connection with which is interesting as showing his interest in new art
forms.   His version of the above little piece
was published, under the title of *The Dispraise of the Life of a Courtier and a commendacioun of the life of the labouryng man,*
in 1548.   It was reproduced by one Thomas
Tymme in 1575 as *A Looking Glasse for the
Court.*   Bryan, like his uncle and North, used

a French intermediary, the version of Antony Allaygre (or Allègre) written in 1542. It is interesting to note that Allègre took a leaf out of Guevara's book, and declared that he published his version only because a scrivener had stolen it. This modest device is a common one in Elizabethan literary history, and later Grub Street knew it well. Hallam preferred this piece to *The Diall*, but the two are too unequal in length to be comparable. The theme, which is revealed in the title, is touched on in the second book of *The Diall* and also in the fourth (the *Aviso*).

The year 1575 saw also the publication of *The Golden Epistles | contayning | varietie of discourse | both Morall, Philosophicall and Divine | gathered, as wel out of the remaynder of | Guevaraes workes, as other Au- | thors, Latine French and Italian | by Geffrey Fenton.*

The author of this, Sir Geoffrey Fenton, is better known as the author of a volume of translations from the Italian Bandello, called *Tragical Discourses* (which include the tale of Romeo and Juliet), but the gold of these epistles cannot be appraised very high. That other editions were called for in 1557 and 1582 is a tribute to the popularity of anything bearing Guevara's name. Fenton did not tell his readers which of his pages were taken from Guevara and which from ' other authors.'

But Guevara's most devoted disciple was Edward Hellowes, Groom of her Majesty's Leash, to whose credit stand three and possibly four items, to wit :

(1) Familiar Epistles, 1574.
(2) A chronicle conteyning the lives of tenne Emperors of Rome, 1577.
(3) Book of the Arte of Navigation, 1577.

And to him Senor Galvez ascribes :

(4) The Mount of Calvaria, 1595.

None of these adds much to Guevara's reputation, or makes one for Hellowes. Here, too, a French intermediary is expressly confessed to in the case of the *Chronicle* and may safely be assumed, therefore, in the case of the others. Hellowes' style is stiff and not a little clumsy, as a brief specimen from the *Chronicle* will show :

' In the second yeare of the Empire of the good Vespasian, Great Britaine rebelled which is now named England against the Romaine Emperour : unto which warrs Trajane repaired, and this he did without charges to the Romaines, and for himself to obtaine fame accompanied with many others of his countrie : In those warres Drusius

Torquatus was captaine for the Romaines : who persuading Trajane to take wages of the Romaine people, as all others did injoy in that warres, Trajane answered : The merchants that come from thence hither, they repaire to be more rich, but we Gentlemen not to be richer, but more honoured.'

Guevara does not tell anecdotes badly, and Hellowes does him less than justice. The Familiar Letters are not very lively reading. So far from being written, as might have been hoped, in the style of Cicero or Pliny, they are largely moral discourses and dissertations (fortunately brief) on points of antiquarian interest. But three editions were printed within ten years, and one hundred years later we find them translated again by one Savage, under the auspices of that indefatigable bookman and journalist, Sir Roger l'Estrange.

§ 7

It is on the *Relox* in Spain, or in England on *The Diall*, that Guevara's fame must rest. If the earlier and shorter book be preferred to it, it is only because both are accounted wearisome, and so the less the reader has of either the better. For there is no symmetry of form in the original draft to be lost in the

expanded version. They are the same commodity sold by the peck or by the bushel.
The book is, as the short account of its
genesis given above indicates, formed round
a nucleus of Marcus Aurelius, his Life and
Letters. But the proportions are not dis-
similar to those usual between kernel and
nut. The whole is a farrago of dissertations,
with copious anecdotes and quotations (the
best of them from Plutarch, but not, in
North's own way, bettered in the telling)
concerning princes, what they have done
and what they ought and ought not to do.
And incidentally almost anything Guevara
has ever heard or can imagine about tribal
customs or popular superstitions can be
made grist for his windmill. There is no
central line of argument, and it would
scarcely be possible, even if it were worth
while, to extract from the book a system-
atised theory of statecraft. The book gains,
rather than loses, by being read in selections,
or dipped into here and there for a chance
piece of moralising or a stray anecdote. All
pretence of a history is gone. It is ridiculous
and suggestive of a complete lack of first-
hand acquaintance with the text to call it,
as some writers do, a ' didactic novel.' The

three books represent subject groups, not phases or periods in the emperor's life ; and except that his upbringing is mentioned in the first book and his death in the third, there is no attempt at a chronological narrative. The fourth book upsets even this slender pretence of a biographic scheme, but this is not Guevara's doing.

The book as a whole is formless and is most charitably regarded as a loose collection of essays. It is also unconscionably long. The 1582 edition of *The Diall* contains 1000 small quarto pages, by our modern reckoning, of very closely set black-letter type, and it is not only the multiplication of the units that makes the book so long, but the copiousness with which each point is treated. Guevara's own account of his method is that he took a speech or a letter of Marcus as his text and added reflections of his own and parallel instances. These texts are often extremely long, and the preacher's embellishments are still longer. It is not therefore wonderful that succeeding ages, which had more books to read and less patience to listen to much citing of ancient authorities in support of principles that were by that time either trite or exploded, ceased to read the ' eloquent

oratour.' Shakespeare might well have said
of him, as he makes one of his characters say
of another Spaniard, ' He draweth out the
thread of his verbosity finer than the staple
of his argument.'

Yet there is still much in *The Diall* that
may be read to-day both with profit and with
pleasure. Guevara had really lived long at
the court of the greatest of contemporary
monarchs, and he had seen a good deal of
other countries as well. And his good sense,
when it is not obscured under a mountain of
citations, is conspicuously admirable. Guevara is writing for an autocrat, and even
when he speaks hardly of the faults of the
princely caste, he has to make it clear that
these things are but specks on the sun and
do not betoken any evil in the institution of
kingship. But the Bishop is no sycophant.
His advice is often salutary and not, if we
remember his age and country, lacking in
courageous originality. He advocates a
benevolent autocracy, but writes with genuine
passion on the evils of wars of conquest, and
on the responsibilities of those in high place.
He rebukes excessive national pride in a
manner particularly notable in a Spaniard.
His disparagement of courts and his praise

of the simple life is plainly in a great measure sincere.

And on practical points he is admirable. His advice as to dress, horsemanship, table manners, and other like matters would furnish forth a serviceable handbook for the 'temporary gentleman' of to-day. On wines and on cooking he speaks with evident authority, and while condemning with churchmanlike severity the seven deadly sins, he does not refuse to admit the existence of lawful pleasures not strictly within the limits of the cardinal virtues. Moreover, there is little of the proverbial Inquisitor about this member of the Toledo Council, and though his portrait of Marcus Aurelius is quite unauthentic, he cannot have been wholly of a different mind from that tolerant and virtuous Stoic. His treatment of Comparative Mythology was fanciful and inaccurate, but it does not argue the fanatical dogmatist.

Finally, there is no doubt but that Guevara was a confirmed and temperamental old bachelor. His homilies on chastity arc sane and sound, and he has some wise and acute things to say on the perennial theme of Love ; but though constantly advocating courtesy and respect for woman, he too obviously regards her as man's inferior, and for the most part as a thorn in his flesh. He is not always, however, quite so unbearable in his attitude towards her as the words he puts into the mouth of Marcus Aurelius in his colloquy with Faustine. The emperor there shows himself as intolerably patronising as he is interminably prolix, and even those who sympathise with a good deal of the matter will admit the tactlessness of the manner. This passage, here given *in extenso*, was one of the most famous in the book, but it was surpassed by the speech of the villain of the Danube, which is also given. This personage is quite often referred to by old writers, and La Fontaine reproduced him in his *Paysan du Danube*. Some of his utterances have a casual but curious appositeness to-day.

Another passage here printed, the episode of Sinoris and Camma, is the original of one of the stories in Pettie's famous collection, his *Pettie Palace of Pleasure*. Pettie's version is a longer and more ornate but not a more effective telling of the tale. The passage from *The Favourite of the Court* is one of the most entertaining in the work, giving a valuable picture of the manners and customs of the day. But an infinity of readable pages could be chosen. The only trouble with Guevara is that there is, in bulk, too much of him. Nor is this due to mere garrulousness : it is an essential element in his style. To say the same thing in several ways is his method of establishing the truth of a general proposition: simple enumeration is his favourite proof. His interminable web of moralising and anecdotage is not ornament overlaid upon a ground of plain argument. It is the very fabric of his work. He does achieve the successful utterance of many rotund phrases and a few wise sentences, but at the cost of a prodigious deal of wind.

To the modern reader who likes wise saws expressed more pithily than Guevara's, the instances from Plutarch, Suetonius, and other ancient authors, with an occasional draft on his own experience, will be the most entertaining part of his writings. Of these he is prodigal, sometimes sacrificing quality and appositeness to quantity and wide range : he is a *gourmand* rather than a *gourmet* at the banquet of ancient wisdom. His chief source is Plutarch, whose *Moralia* he uses even more than his *Lives*, and he had undoubtedly read very widely in Latin and in translations from

the Greek, of which tongue he confesses his
ignorance. He quotes from nearly all the
extant histories of Greece and Rome, particularly the later and lesser ones ; such as
Suetonius, Diogenes Laertius, Valerius Maxi-
mus, Herodian, Lampridius and his fellows,
together with such writings as Philostratus'
Apollonius of Tyana, the letters of Phalaris,
Anacharsis, and a host of others. But he is
quite reckless in the names he appends to his
innumerable anecdotes. In his own century
the learned Rhua [1] protested against his un-
scholarly romancing, and his latest Spanish
editor [2] admits that he has mingled true and
false quotations and ascriptions beyond all
unravelling. But he tells his stories plainly
and briefly, and he who dips here and there
into his books will usually find something to
afford amusement and even edification.

§ 8

But it is the style rather than the matter
that interests the critics of later days, and
was probably the real attraction to Guevara's
contemporaries. As Guevara himself sug-

[1] Pedro de Rhua, *Curtas sobre las obras del . . . obispo de
Mondoñedo*, 1549.
[2] M. Martinez de Burgos.

gests, the style was the piquant sauce that rendered such a great mass of material palatable and digestible. But the modern interest in the matter is historical, for in what Hallam called the ' sententious and antithetical ' style of Guevara is supposed to be the source of all that ornateness in prose writing which, in England, is connected with the name of John Lyly's famous *Euphues*. So generally has this theory been accepted that ' Euphuism ' and ' Guevarism ' are often used as equivalent terms.

This theory was advanced most forcibly by the German Landmann, in his book *Das Euphuismus* (1881) and other writings, and a host of German and American writers of dissertations have enlarged upon his text. But they by no means agree among themselves, some saying that it was Berners and some North who popularised the style, and the claim is by no means proved. It has never been so wholeheartedly admitted by natives as by strangers.

Guevara certainly was one of the earliest European writers to realise that prose was not merely an instrument, to be used anyhow so long as certain statements were made, but that it has its pattern, even as verse has, and possesses a beauty, not independent of its matter, but yet individual ; intensifying the qualities of the abstract thought by the sound and the rhythm, in brief, by the texture of the medium of expression. It was a discovery inevitable in that age, when the æsthetic quality of Ciceronian Latin and Attic Greek was beginning to be appreciated and distinguished from the jargon of the schoolmen and the impure style of the first Humanists ; and we cannot award Guevara more than a share, with many others, of the praise.

Moreover the special qualities of Euphuism, as defined by Landmann himself and his followers, are not all present in Guevara or his translators ; and the assertion that these qualities are developments of certain others which are present is a very hazardous one. Landmann, who rightly admits the existence of Euphuism before *Euphues* (of which the title is borrowed from Ascham), admits also the influence on it of the classics. But he claims that the indigenous English method of imitating the classics is to be seen in Gabriel Harvey, Stanyhurst, and the ' gross eccentricities of Chapman.' With all these extravagances, he declares, ' Euphuism has

nothing to do. . . . " Parisonic antithesis "
and the use of rhetorical figures are its char-
acteristics, and for this quaint style Europe
is indebted to a Spanish writer, Don Antonio
de Guevara, who was perhaps the most in-
fluential writer of Charles the Fifth's reign.'
Of his works, he goes on, the *Relox* was the
most popular, and ' it owes this popularity
to the "high style" in which it was written.'
Berners, he declares, ' did not so closely
imitate Guevara's style as Sir Thomas North,'
who ' was not a mere translator but success-
fully tried to reproduce the rhythmic cadence
of Guevara's parisonic, antithetical clauses, . . .
He did not merely translate from the Spanish
original, and his style exhibits to a much
higher degree than Berners' the specific
elements of Guevarism and Euphuism, viz.
parison, antithesis, and above all transverse
alliteration.'

Now this concentration on North rather
than on Berners as the chief source of
Euphuism makes Landmann's task very
hard, for it is possible to point to frequent
examples of almost all the euphuistic qualities
in Pettie, Paynter, Ascham, and other writers
long before 1557. Others, therefore, have
attempted to shift the weight of the argument

on to Berners, but even so the thesis is hard
to maintain.

Alliteration, in some form or other, is a
marked feature in the English writers. Landmann, as quoted above, claims it as the
distinctive feature of Euphuism. Yet he
writes, ' Guevara certainly used no alliteration.' On the other hand, every Englishman
knows that alliteration is the earliest ornament of his country's verse and had long been
employed in its prose. Even the ' transverse '
form (that is, two initial sounds used chias-
mus fashion) is to be found in Middle English.
Landmann's theory, therefore, that euphuistic alliteration is grown from the seed of
Guevara's ' parisonic antithesis ' (mostly a
matter of similar endings) is a needless and
untenable hypothesis.

And the other alleged prominent charac-
teristics of Guevara's English followers can
with equal ease be traced to good native
stock. ' Parallelism of sentences ' is one of
them. Perhaps the German scholars think
that it was only after Luther's day that
Englishmen could read, ' At her feet he bowed,
he fell, he lay down : at her feet he bowed, he
fell : where he bowed, there he fell down
dead.' Landmann, whose knowledge though

misapplied is considerable, writes, 'The Classics taught Guevara and were teaching England, and doubtless the Bible would have lent its aid. But as it was, Guevara's example taught the Euphuist.' But why 'would have'? In any case, this device and also the duplication of epithets and adverbs (*e.g.* 'all ye that do truly and earnestly repent') is a feature of Old English prose as early as the Venerable Bede!

Other traits in Guevara which Landmann says were borrowed by Lyly and his fellows are : Comparisons from nature, and a predilection for ancient mythology and history. By this reasoning half the literature of the Middle Ages would have to be credited to a prophetic foreknowledge of Guevara. The more special borrowing by Lyly from Guevara (according to Landmann) include the following :

The frivolous daughter of Marcus and Faustine is called Lucilla. So is the heroine of *Euphues*. Also a Livia occurs in both books.

A beekeeper's life is extolled in *Euphues*. This is a plagiarism from the *Commendacioun of the Life of a Labouryng Man*.

The Diall (and also *The Golden Boke*) contains a letter 'to the Enamoured Ladies of Rome.' Lyly wrote 'a cooling carde for Philautus and all fond lovers.' Both inveigh against the fair sex.

Both write passages in imitation of Plutarch's *de Educatione*, and (says Landmann) 'elsewhere I have pointed out two instances in which he word for word follows Plutarch, whose Morals had already been Guevara's principal source.'

This last suggests a new axiom: 'Things that are imitations of the same thing are imitations of one another.'

Landmann even hazards the assertion that 'the idea of compiling his *Euphues* was suggested to him by Guevara's book': a most improbable thing and quite beyond demonstration. 'The plot of *Euphues*,' he says, 'is an imitation of that of *The Diall*.' The plot of *Euphues* is meagre, that of *The Diall* practically non-existent.

There are a few more like items, of no greater validity. Taken singly no ordinary reader would even remark on them as coincidences. Even as cumulative proof they would not have stood for a moment against the fact that no English reader would ever class *The Diall* along with *Euphues*, if *The*

Diall had had any English readers; and even if the plots and characters were alike, that fact would have no bearing on the styles, which are as different as those of any two writers of the same period will ordinarily be.

It is interesting to note the influence of Guevara on those who came into direct contact with him or his writings. Of Berners, Saintsbury (*History of English Prose Rhythm*) writes, 'already, especially in the less ambitious and less bedizened Arthur piece, there is balance, rhythm, accompaniment of sound to sense.' Berners is a more pompous writer than North, but he is no Euphuist, and there is no reason to suppose that his style, which of course was formed before he came to translate Guevara, owes anything to the Spanish writer. Landmann, as we have seen, disowns him.

Bryan was an ' Italianato,' and a contributor to Tottel's *Miscellany.* Any graces in his prose style may be most easily explained as a transference to that medium of his ' sugared sonnet ' style.

Elyot, who met Guevara, was a much better scholar than he, a deliberate reformer of his own language, and a very fine writer, but no Guevarist. Neither was Fenton, whose fame

rests on his translations from the Italian and
not from the Spanish, nor Hellowes, who
was not a distinguished writer.

North, reproducing literally Guevara's
matter, necessarily reproduces many qualities
of his style, particularly the tropes; but
there is little trace of Guevarism in his
Plutarch. Finally, even if Guevara's style
on the one hand and Lyly's on the other were
far nearer to North's than they really are,
there would still be an obstacle to the theory
that the current flowed from one to the other.
Between Guevara's Spanish and the English
of all his translators is interposed a non-
conducting substance. None of the French
translators, on whom all the English versions
are based, troubled to reproduce the ' parisonic antithesis and well-balanced juxta-
position or contraposition of words and
clauses ' on which Landmann builds so much.
No one has ever even claimed that they did.
Other critics have traced other pedigrees for
Euphuism. Dr. Morris Croll, for example,
thinks that its ' homoioteleuton ' and ' poly-
ptoton ' are derived from the mediæval
rhetoricians and writers of sermons and lives
of the saints. That may well be, but it
does not concern us here. It is enough to

note that he discards the Guevaristic theory.

To dogmatize on such a matter is dangerous, but the plain man will probably not admit more than some such conclusion as this :

Devices already common in verse and also in rhetorical pieces, and derived largely from the classical writers, were being introduced into the ordinary prose of all the European languages. According to the genius of their several tongues and their own tastes, various writers emphasised various devices, but a great number of these are the common tools of all the craftsmen of the age. In England, alliteration was an indigenous national device, and the languages of the true Classics were just becoming widely known, while the Bible was, through Tyndale's version (which succeeded Wyclif's), exercising an ever-growing influence. There are certain broad features in Guevara's style which jumped with the taste of the time (though it was by no means everybody's taste). *The Golden Boke* and *The Diall of Princes* were both popular books, and their influence would certainly strengthen the cognate elements in contemporary English prose. But they cannot be shown to be more than tributaries, among others flowing into those same reaches, of that great and many channelled stream.

§ 9

The present selection represents barely a tithe of the entire *Diall*, but the passages chosen represent both the strong and the weak points of the book. All the best known episodes have been included. A more entertaining volume might have been prepared of short anecdotes and apophthegms, but that would not give by any means so just an idea of what this famous book, valuable if only as an index to the literary taste of Tudor times, really was. The Table of the original book is reprinted in full as the best brief indication of its compass and true nature. An asterisk denotes chapters reproduced in this version. In Appendices will be found brief specimens of Guevara's Spanish and Berthault's French, and also of the other English translators, Berners, Bryan, and Fenton. A passage from Hellowes will be found above, p. xxii.

The spelling of *The Diall*, after some hesitation, has been modernised ; the punctuation, which is probably more useful as a guide to

North's rhythm than to his syntax, has been altered only where it obscured the sense or where modern usage has introduced entirely new features (*e.g.* inverted commas).

The paragraphs in the original, which are fewer than modern judgment requires, are indicated by a ¶.

The text is based on that of the 1582 Quarto.

K. N. C.

Note on North's French Source (p. xix).

I do not think North used Berthault's version. He might have used an edition of de Herberay earlier than any I have seen. Such certainly existed, for the title-page of the 1561 edition states that it is 'en partie reveu & corrige nouvellement outre toutes les autres precedentes impressions.' It is significant that at the end of Bk. III. chap. iii. the Spanish text and Berthault read *Romanorum est expoliare innocentes et inquietare quietos* (B., *quietes*), whereas de Herberay and North read *et reddere subjectos* for the last three words. But the Fourth Book is not in de Herberay, and North, in his Epistle to the Reader prefaced thereto, speaks of ' the translation of the late & new-come favored courtier (and which I found annexed to the Dial for the iiii & last booke).' The appended letters are described as 'not written in the French tongue,' so that North seems to have been capable of using the Spanish original. I have not seen a Spanish edition with the *Aviso* incorporated. North's version of the Fourth Book appears to be independent of Rochemore's *Le Favori de Court.*

BIBLIOGRAPHY

FOR a full bibliography of Guevara's writings in Spanish see ' Bibliographie Espagnole de Fray Antonio de Guevara,' by R. Foulche-Delbosc. New York and Paris, 1915.

For a shorter bibliography of both Spanish and English books see ' Guevara in England : Kapitel I. and II.,' by Jose Maria Galvez. (Berlin University dissertation, 1910.) This is also printed as an introduction to the same editor's reprint of the ' Golden Boke.' (Palaestra CIX. Berlin, 1916.)

The following are some of the most important Guevara items :

.I. Libro aureo de Mar | co Aurelio : empera | dor : y eloquentis | simo orador | Nuevamente | impresso.   Seville, 1528.   Fol.

(The colophon of this runs : ' Fue impresso en la noble y muy leal ciudad de sevilla por Jacobo Croberger Alema. Ano de Señor de mill y quincientos y veynte y ocho. Acabose en xxvii de Febrero.' This copy is in the Biblioteca Nacional, Madrid.)

do.   Saragossa, 1529.   Fol.
do.   Paris, 1529.   4°.
do.   Antwerp, 1529.   4°.

Editions were also published in the following years : 1532 (2), 1533, 1536, 1539, 1545, 1546, 1550, 1553, 1555, 1566 (2), 1569, 1574, 1594, 1596, 1604, 1624, 1647.

Of the Portuguese edition of 1528 no copies exist.

The French translation of the above is :

Livre d'ore de Marc Aurele . . . par R(ene)
B(erthault) de la Grife. Paris, 1531. 4°.
      do.   do. 1549. 8°.

The English translation of this is :

The Golden Boke of Marcus Aurelius Emperor and
Eloquent Oratour. London, 1535. 4°.
      do.   do. 1536. 4°.
      do.   do. 1539. 4°.
      (Colophon dated 1538.)

Quarto editions were also published in 1542 and 1546,
and 8° editions in 1553, 1557, 1559, 1566, 1573, 1586 :
all in Black Letter. (The 1535 and 1536 editions are
not in the British Museum, but there are copies in the
Bodleian.)

II. Libro de Emperador Marco aurelio co relox de
principes : auctor del qual es el obispo de
Guadix. Valladolid, 1529. Fol.
      do. Seville, 1531. Fol.
      do. Barcelona, 1532. Fol.
      do. Seville, 1532. Fol.

Editions were also published in the following years :
1534, 1535 (?), 1537, 1543, 1550, 1557, 1650, 1651, 1658,
1675, 1698.

The French translation of the above is :

Lorloge des Princes (tr. by Berthault).
      Paris, 1540. Fol.
      do.   do. Rennes, 1540. Fol.
      do.   do. Paris, 1550. 8°.

Editions were also published in 1552, 1576, 1592.

L'Horloge des Princes avec le tres-renomme livre
de Marc Aurele (tr. by N. de Herberay).
      Paris, 1561. 8°.
      do.   do. Paris, 1566. 8°.

The English translation of this is :

The Diall | of Princes | Compiled by the rever-
ende father in | God, DON ANTHONY of
GUEVARA, Bys | shop of GUADIX Preacher
and Cro | nicler, to Charles the fyft Em | perour
of Rome | Englysshed oute of the Frenche,
by | THOMAS NORTH, second sonne | of the
LORDE NORTH.

Ryght necessary and pleasaunt to all | Gentyl-
men and others whiche | are lovers of virtue. |
Anno 1557 | ¶ *Imprinted at London by John
Waylande.* | *Cum privilegio, ad imprimendum
solum per septennium.*
[This contains 3 books and additional letters.]
                              London, 1557. Fol.

The Diall of Princes . . . Englyshed . . . by
Thomas North . . . with an amplification also
of a fourth booke entituled The Favored
Courtier. . . .   London, 1568. Fol.
        do.   London, 1582. 4°.

ΑΡΧΟΝΤΟΡΟΛΟΓΙΟΝ | or | the | Diall | of |
Princes | containing | The Golden and Famous |
Booke of Marcus | Aurelius, sometime Em-
perour of Rome | Declaring | what excellency
insisteth in a Prince that is a good Christian :
and what evils | attend on him that is a cruell
Tirant. | Written | By the Reverend Father in
God, Don Antonio of Guevara, Lord | Bishop
of Guadix ; Preacher and Chronicler to the
late mighty Emperour | Charles the fift | First
translated out of French by Thomas North,
sonne to Sir Edward North, Lord North of |
Kirthling : And lately reperused, and cor-
rected from | many grosse imperfections |

With addition of a Fourth Booke, stiled by
the Name of | The Favoured Courtier.

London, 1619. Fol.

III. Aviso de Privados [in Obras de Guevara].

Valladolid, 1539. Fol.

Libro llamado aviso de privados.

Pamplona, 1579. 8°.

The French translation of the above is :

Le favory de court, tr. by J. de Rochemore.

Lyon, 1556. 8°·

do. C. Plantin : Anvers, 1557. 8°.

The English translation of this is the fourth
book of North's Diall of Princes, ' The
Favourcd Courtier.' London, 1568. Fol.
(and subsequent editions, *vide supra*).

IV. Epistolas Familiares (3 books) [in Obras de
Guevara]. Valladolid, 1539. Fol.
Epistolas Familiares : Segunda Parte.

Valladolid, 1541. Fol.

The French version of the above is :
Epitres Dorees moralles et familieres. Tom. 1
and 2, tr. by le Seigneur Guterry. Tom. 3
[by A. du Pinet]. 3 vols. Lyon, 1556-60. 4°.
do. do. 1588. 8°.

English versions of portions of the above are :

Familiar Epistles of Sir | Anthony of Guevara,
Preacher | Chronicler, and Counceller to the |
Emperour Charles the fifth | Translated out of
the Spanish toung by Edward Hellowes,
Groome of the Leashe. . . . London, [1574]. 4°.
do. London, 1577. 4°.
do. London, 1584. 4°.

Golden Epistles . . . gathered as well out of
the remaynder of Guevaraes woorkes, as other
Authours, Latin, French, and Italian by
Geoffrey Fenton.   London, 1575.   4°.
   do.   do.   London, 1577.   4°.
   do.   do.   London, 1582.   4°.
(The 1575 edition of this is not in the British Museum,
but there is a copy in the Guildhall Library.)

Spanish Letters, historical, sattyrical & moral
. . . recommended by Sir R. L. S. & made
English from the best originals by Mr. Savage.
          London, 1697.   8°.

Spanish Letters . . . 1520-5, made English
by John Savage.   London, n.d.   8°.
   (This is in the Bodleian.)

Letters of Wit, Politicks & Morality, written
in Italian by the famous Cardinal Bentivoglio,
in Spanish by Signior Don Guevara, etc., done
into English by the Honourable H   . H   .,
Esq., Tho. Cheek, Esq., Mr. Savage, Mr.
Boyer, etc.   Part III. contains Select Letters
Historical, Satyrical & Moral written in Spanish
by the famous Don Antonio de Guevara . . .
made English by Mr. Savage (10 letters).
Part IV. contains 3 further letters.   These
are from ' Spanish Letters.'   London, 1701.   8°.

V. Menosprecio de Corte y Alabanza de Aldea
   . . . (in Obras de Guevara).
          Valladolid, 1539.   Fol.
  Libro llamado Menosprecio de Corte y Ala-
   bança de Aldea . . .   [Antwerp, 1550 ?]   8°.
     do.   Pamplona, 1579.   8°.
     do.   Alcala de Henares, 1592.   8°.
  Ed. Martinez de Burgos (with introduction)
   in ' Clasicos Castellanos.   Ediciones de " La
   Letura." '   Madrid, 1915.   8°.

Editions in Spanish, French, and Italian were also
published in 1591 (16°) and 1614 (12°).

The French version of the above is :

Le Mespris de Court. Tr. by A. Allègre.

Paris, 1542. 8°.

do.   Paris, 1556. 16°.

English translations of this are :

Dispraise of the Life of a Courtier & a commendacioun of the life of the labouryng man.
Translated by Sir F. Bryan(t).

London, 1548. 8°.

A Looking Glasse for the Court composed in the
Castilian tongue by the Lorde Anthony of
Guevara . . . and out of Castilian drawne into
Frenche by Anthony Alaygre and out of the
Frenche tongue into Englishe by Sir Fraunces
Briant Knight one of the privy chamber, in the
raygne of K. Henry the eyght and now newly
printed corrected and set forth with sundry apt
notes in the margent by T. Tymme.

London, 1575. 8°.

VI. Una decada de las vidas de los X Cesares
Emperadores romanos, desde Trajano a
Alexandro [in Obras de Guevara].

Valladolid, 1539. Fol.

do.   Anvers, 1544.   8°.

The English version of this is :

A Chronicle, conteyning the lives of tenne
Emperors of Rome. Tr. by Edward Hellowes.

London, 1577. 4°.

VII. De los inventores del marear y de muchos
trabajos que se passan en las galeras [in
Obras de Guevara.]   Valladolid, 1539.

The English version of this is :

A Booke of the Invention of the Arte of
Navigation.   Tr. by Edward Hellowes.
London, 1577.   4°.
do.   London, 1578.   4°.

VIII. La primera parte del libro llamado Monte
Calvario . . . Trata de todos los mys-
terios de Monte Calvario . . .
Valladolid, 1545.   Fol. and 4°.
La segunda parte del libro, etc.
Valladolid, 1549.   Fol. and 4°.
The French translation of this is :
Livre du Mont de Calvarie.   Tr. by de Belle-
Forest.   Paris, 1578.   8°.
The English translation of this is :
The Mount of Calvarie . . . Wherin is handled
all the mysteries of the Mount of Calvarie,
from the time that Christ was condemned by
Pilat, until he was put into the sepulcher, by
Joseph and Nichodemus. [This is the first part
only.]   [Tr. by Edward Hellowes ?]
London, 1595.   4°.
Mount Calvarie, the second part . . . of the
seven words which Christ . . . spake hanging
upon the crosse.   Translated out of Spanish
into English.   London, 1597.   4°.
do.   The First part (2nd edition).
London, 1618.   4°.

IX. Oratorio de religiosos y exercicio de virtuosos.
1542.   Fol.

Libro llamado Oratorio de, etc.
Çaragoça, 1543.   Fol.
do.   Valladolid, 1546.   Fol.

THE DIALL OF PRINCES

TO THE MOST HIGH AND VIRTUOUS
PRINCESS, MARY, BY THE GRACE OF
GOD, QUEEN OF ENGLAND, SPAIN,
FRANCE, BOTH SICILIES, JERUSALEM,
NAPLES, AND IRELAND, DEFENDER OF
THE FAITH, ARCHDUCHESS OF AUSTRIA,
DUCHESS OF BURGUNDY, MILAN AND
BRABANT, COUNTESS OF HAPSBURG,
FLANDERS AND TYROL, LONG HEALTH
AND PERPETUAL FELICITY.

¶ The Divine Philosopher Plato, most
gracious sovereign Lady, travailing all his
life time to abolish the barbarous manners
of the Grecians and to induce a civil form
of living among the people, ordained a law
to the great comfort of those that followed
virtue and no less to the terror of others
that haunted vices. The which commanded,
that not only those which brought in or invented any new thing that might either corrupt the good manners, violate the ancient
customs, hinder through evil example good
living, impoison with erroneous doctrine
the consciences, effeminate with voluptuous
pleasures the hearts, impoverish with un-

profitable merchandise the people or defame with malicious words the renowns, should be (as unprofitable members) from the common wealth expelled and banished : but also ordained that those which studied to publish any institution appertaining either to the honour of the gods, to the reformation of the frailty of men, or by any other means to the profit of the weal public, should be condignly of the common wealth entertained, preferred and honoured.

Then, if this law were just, most gracious sovereign Lady (as it is most just indeed), who deserved more honourable entertainment among the living, or who meriteth a worthier fame among the dead, than Don Antony of Guevara the author hereof ? For, by his staid life God hath been glorified, by his wholesome doctrine the people of Spain heretofore edified, and by his sweet and savoury writings, we (and sundry other nations) at this present may be much profited. The which, though they are all pithy and full of high doctrine, yet this entitled Lo relox de principes above the rest (in my opinion) is most profound and pleasant, for, if the zeal that I bear to his works deceive not my judgment, there is no author (the sacred letters set apart) that more effectually setteth out the omnipotency of God, the frailty of men, the inconstancy of fortune, the vanity of this world, the misery of this life and finally that more plainly teacheth the good which mortal men ought to pursue and the evil that all men ought to fly, than this present work doth. The which is so full of high doctrine, so adorned with ancient histories, so authorized with grave sentences and so beautified with apt similitudes, that I know not whose eyes in reading it can be wearied, nor whose ears in hearing it not satisfied.

/ Considering therefore (most gracious sovereign Lady) that this work may serve to high estates for counsel, to curious searchers of antiquities for knowledge, and to all other virtuous gentlemen for an honest, pleasant and profitable recreation, and finally that it may profit all and can hurt none : I (according to my small knowledge and tender years) have reduced it into our vulgar tongue, and under Your Grace's name have published it for the commodity of many, most humbly beseeching Your Highness to accept in good part (according to Your Grace's accustomable goodness) this my good will and travail : which here I offer as a pledge of my bounden duty towards Your Highness, and also as a perpetual memory of the fervent zeal I bear to my country. And in so doing Your Grace shall not only encourage me, being young, in these my first fruits : but also others (peradventure) of more ripe years, to attempt the like enterprise, by which the divine majesty may be immortally glorified, your puissant name worthily magnified, your royal person duly obeyed, and all Your Grace's natural and loving subjects greatly profited.

At Lincoln's Inn the 20th of December.

Your Highness' most humble and loyal subject THOMAS NORTH.

THE TABLE OF
'THE DIALL OF PRINCES'

The Prologue general of the Author.
The Prologue upon the book entitled Marcus
  Aurelius.
The Argument of the whole book.

[1] The first chapter entreateth of the birth and lineage of Marcus Aurelius, where the Author reciteth at the beginning of the book three chapters in the which he declareth the discourse of his life : for by his epistles and doctrine this whole work is proved.

[2] Of a letter which Marcus Aurelius wrote to his friend Pulio, wherein he recounteth the order of his life, and, among other things, declareth the words which a poor man of Nola spake unto the Roman Censor.

[3] Marcus Aurelius concludeth his letter and mentioneth the sciences which he learned and all the masters he had and in the end he reciteth five notable things in the observance of the which the Romans were very curious.

[4] Of the excellency of the Christian religion (whereby the true God is known) and of the vanities of the Ancients in times past.

[5] How among the Ancients the philosopher Bruxellus was esteemed, and of the words he spake unto them at the hour of his death.

[6] Of the words which Bruxellus the philosopher spake to the Senate of Rome.

[7] How the Gentiles thought that one God was not of power sufficient to defend them from their enemies.

[8] Of a letter which the Senate sent unto all those which were subject to the Empire.

[9] Of the true and living God and of the marvels He wrought in the old law to manifest His divine power and of the superstition of the false gods.

[10] That there is but one true God and how that Realm is happy which hath a king that is a good Christian.

[11] Of sundry gods which the Ancients worshipped, of the office of those gods, and how they were revenged of those that displeased them.

[12] Of other more natural and peculiar gods which the ancient people had.

[13] How Tiberius the Knight was chosen Governor of the Empire and afterwards created Emperor, only for being a good Christian : how God deprived Justinian the Younger both of his senses and empire for being an heretic.

[14] Of the words the Empress Sophia spake to Tiberius Constantine, which tended to his reproof for that he consumed the treasures which she had gathered.

[15] The answer of Tiberius unto the Empress Sophia wherein he declareth that princes need not to hoard up great treasures.

[16] How the chieftain Narsetes overcame many battles, only for that his whole confidence was in God. And what happened to him by the Empress Sophia Augusta : wherein may be noted the unthankfulness of princes towards their servants.

[17] Of a letter the Emperor Marcus Aurelius sent to the King of Sicily, in the which he recordeth the travails they endured together in their youth and reproveth him of his small reverence towards the temples.

[18] The Emperor proceedeth in his letter to ad- Book I monish princes to be fearful of their gods and of the sentence which the Senate gave upon this king for pulling down the church.

[19] How the Gentiles honoured those which were devout in the service of the gods.

[20] For five causes princes ought to be better Christians than their subjects.

[21] Of the philosopher Bias and of the ten laws which he gave, worthy to be had in mind.

[22] How God, from the beginning, punished evil men by His justice and specially those princes that despise His church and mansion house.

[23] The author proveth by twelve examples that princes are sharply punished when they usurp boldly upon the churches and violate the temples.

[24] How Valentine the Emperor because he was an evil Christian lost in one day both the Empire and his life and was burned alive in a sheepcote.

[25] Of the Emperor Valentinian and Gratian his son, which, because they were good Christians were always fortunate and that God giveth victories unto princes more through tears of them that pray, than through the weapons of those that fight.

[26] Of the godly oration which the Emperor Gratian made to his soldiers before he gave the battle.

[27] That the Captain Theodosius (which was father of the great Emperor Theodosius) died a good Christian: of the King Hysmarus and the Bishop Silvanus and the holy laws which they made and established.

[28] What a goodly thing it is to have but one prince to rule in the public weal, for there is no greater enemy to the common weal than he which procureth many to command therein.

[29] That in a public weal there is no greater destruction than where princes daily consent to new orders and change old customs.

[30] When tyrants began to reign and upon what occasion commanding and obeying first began : and how the authority the prince hath is by the ordinance of God.

[31] Of the golden age in times past and worldly misery at this present.

[32] What the Garamantes said unto King Alexander the Great when he went to conquer India, and how that the purity of life hath more power than any force of war.

[33] Of an oration which one of the sages of Garamantia made unto King Alexander : a goodly lesson for ambitious men.

[34] The Sage Garamante continueth his oration and, among other notable matters, he maketh mention of seven laws which they observed.

[35] That princes ought to consider for what cause they were made princes, and what Thales the Philosopher was, and of the questions demanded him.

[36] What Plutarch the Philosopher was, the wise words he spake to Traian the Emperor, and how the good prince is the head of the public weal.

[37] The prince ought to hear the complaints of all his subjects and to know them all, to recompense their service.

[38] Of a solemn feast the Romans celebrated to the god Ianus, and of the bounty of the Emperor Marcus Aurelius the same day.

[39] Of the Emperor's answer to Fulvius, the Senator, wherein he painteth envious men.

[40] Of a letter the Emperor Marcus Aurelius wrote Book I
to his friend Pulio, wherein he declareth the opinions
of certain philosophers concerning the felicity of man.

[41] That princes and great lords ought not to esteem
themselves for being fair and well proportioned of
body.

[42] Of a letter which Marcus Aurelius wrote to his
nephew Epesipus, worthy to be noted of all young
gentlemen.

* [43] How princes and noble men, in old time, were
lovers of sages.

[44] How the Emperor Theodosius provideth wise
men at the hour of his death for the education of his
sons.

[45] Cresus, Ling of Lydia, was a great lover of sages :
of a letter the same Cresus wrote to the philosopher
Anacharses and of the philosopher's answer again to
the king.

[46] Of the wisdom and sentence of Phalaris the
Tyrant, and how he put an artisan to death for inventing new torments.

[47] That sundry mighty and puissant princes were
lovers and friends of the sages. ⹀

¶ The Table of the Second Book

[1] Of what excellency marriage is and, whereas
common people marry of free will, princes and noblemen ought to marry of necessity.

[2] How by means of marriage many mortal enemies
have been made perfect friends.

[3] Of the sundry laws the ancients had in contract-
ing matrimony and of the manner of celebrating
marriage.

[4] How princesses and great ladies ought to love their husbands and that must be without any manner of witchcraft or sorcery, but only procured by wisdom and obedience.

* [5] The revenge of a Grecian lady on him that had slain her husband in hope to have her to wife.

[6] That princesses and great ladies should be obedient to their husbands and that it is a great shame to the husband to suffer to be commanded by his wife.

[7] That women (especially princesses and great ladies) should be very circumspect in going abroad out of their houses, and that through the report of them that come to their houses they be not ill spoken of.

[8] Of the commodities and discommodities which follow princesses and great ladies that go abroad to visit, or abide in the house.

[9] That women, great with child (namely princesses and great ladies) ought to be very circumspect for the danger of the creatures they bear: wherein is laid before you many known and sorrowful misfortunes happened to women in that case.

[10] A further rehearsal of other inconveniences and unlucky chances happened to women great with child.

[11] That women, great with child (chiefly princesses and great ladies) ought to be gently entreated of their husbands.

[12] What the Philosopher, Pisto, was, and of the rules he gave concerning women with child.

[13] Of three counsels which Lucius Seneca gave unto a secretary, his friend, who served the Emperor Nero. And how Marcus Aurelius disposed all the hours of the day.

* [14] Of the importunate suit of the Empress Faustine Book II
to the Emperor Marcus Aurelius her husband concerning the key of his closet.

* [15] The Emperor's answer to Faustine touching
the demand of the key of his closet.

* [16] The Emperor followeth his matter, admonishing
men of the plagues and great dangers that follow those
which haunt too much the company of women. And
reciteth also certain rules for married men which, if
they be matched to shrews and do observe them, may
cause them to live in quiet with their wives.

* [17] The Emperor answereth more particularly
concerning the key of his closet.

[18] That princesses and noble women ought not to
be ashamed to give their children suck with their own
breasts.

[19] The author still persuadeth women to give their
own children suck.

[20] That princesses and great ladies ought to be
very circumspect in choosing their nurses : of seven
properties which a good nurse should have.

[21] The author addeth three other conditions to a
good nurse that giveth suck.

[22] Of the disputation before Alexander the Great
concerning the sucking of babes.

[23] Of witchcrafts and sorceries which the nurses
used in old time in giving their children suck.

[24] Marcus Aurelius writeth to his friend Dedalus
inveighing against witches which cure children by
sorceries and charms.

[25] How excellent a thing it is for a gentleman to
have an eloquent tongue.

[26] Of a letter which the Athenians sent to the
Lacedemonians.

Book II   [27] That nurses which gave suck to the children of princes ought to be discreet and sage women.

[28] That women may be no less wise than men and though they be not, it is not through default of nature, but for want of good bringing up.

[29] Of a letter which Pithagoras sent to his sister Theoclea, she reading at that time Philosophy in Samothracia.

[30] The author followeth his purpose persuading princesses and great ladies to endeavour themselves to be wise as the women were in old time.

[31] Of the worthiness of the Lady Cornelia and of a notable epistle she wrote to her two sons Tiberius and Caius, which served in the wars.

[32] Of the education and doctrine of children whilst they are young.

[33] Princes ought to take heed that their children be not brought up in vain pleasures and delights.

[34] That princes and great lords ought to be careful in seeking men to bring up their children. Of ten conditions that good schoolmasters ought to have.

[35] Of the two sons of Marcus Aurelius of the which the eldest and best beloved died. And of the masters he reproved for the other named Commodus.

[36] How Marcus Aurelius rebuked five of the fourteen masters he had chosen for the education of his son Commodus. And how he banished the rest from his palace for their light behaviour at the feast of the god Genius.

[37] That princes and other noble men ought to oversee the tutors of their children lest they conceal the secret faults of their scholars.

[38] Of the Emperor's determination, when he committed his son to the tutors which he had provided for his education.

[39] That tutors of princes and noble men's sons Book II ought to be very circumspect that their scholars do not accustom themselves in vices while they are young, and especially to keep them from four vices.

[40] Of two other vices, perilous in youth, which the masters ought to keep them from.

¶ The Table of the Third Book

[1] How princes and great lords ought to travail to administer to all equal justice.

[2] The way that princes ought to use in choosing their judges and officers in their countries.

* [3] Of an oration which a villain of Danuby made before the Senators of Rome concerning the tyranny and oppressions which their officers used in his country.

* [4] The villain argueth against the Romans, which without cause or reasons conquered their country, and proveth manifestly that they, through offending their gods, were vanquished of the Romans.

* [5] The villain concludeth his oration against the judges which minister not justice and declareth how prejudicial such wicked men are to the common weal.

[6] That princes and noble men should be very circumspect in choosing judges and officers, for therein consisteth the profit of the public weal.

[7] Of a letter which Marcus Aurelius wrote to Antigonus his friend wherein he speaketh against the cruelty of judges and officers.

[8] The Emperor Marcus continueth his letter against cruel judges and reciteth two examples : the one of a pitiful king of Cyprus and the other of a cruel judge of Rome and in this chapter is mentioned the herb Ilabia (growing in Cyprus on the Mount Arcladye) which being cut droppeth blood, etc.

Book III   [9] Of the words which Nero spake concerning justice and of the instruction which the Emperor Augustus gave to a judge which he sent into Dacia.

[10] The Emperor followeth his purpose against cruel judges and declareth a notable embassage which came from India to the Senate of Rome to complain of the judges that governed that realm.

[11] The Emperor concludeth his letter against the cruel judges and declareth what the grandfather of King Boco spake in the Senate.

[12] An exhortation of the author to princes and noble men to embrace peace and to eschew the occasions of war.

* [13] The commodities which come of peace.

* [14] A letter of Marcus Aurelius to his friend Cornelius wherein he describeth the discommodities of war and the vanity of the triumph.

* [15] The Emperor Marcus Aurelius declareth the order that the Romans used in setting forth men of war and of the outrageous villanies which captains and soldiers use in the wars.

* [16] Marcus Aurelius lamenteth with tears the folly of the Romans for that they made war with Asia. And declareth what great damage cometh unto the people where the prince doth begin wars in a strange country.

[17] That princes and great lords (the more they grow in years) should be the more discreet and virtuous to refrain from vices.

[18] That princes when they are aged should be temperate in eating, sober in drinking, modest in apparel, and, above all, true in their communication.

* [19] Of a letter of the Emperor Marcus Aurelius to Claudius and Claudinus wherein he reproveth those that have many years and little discretion.

* [20] The Emperor followeth his letter and persuadeth those that are old to give no more credit to the world nor to any of his flatteries.

* [21] The Emperor proceedeth in his letter, and proveth by good reasons, that since the aged persons will be served and honoured of the young, they ought to be more virtuous and honest than the young.

* [22] The Emperor concludeth his letter and showeth what perils those old men live in which dissolutely, like young children, pass their days and giveth unto them the wholesome counsel for the remedy thereof.

[23] Princes ought to take heed that they be not noted of avarice, for that the covetous man is both of God and man hated.

[24] The author followeth his matter and giveth great reasons discommending the vices of covetous men.

[25] Of a letter which the Emperor Marcus Aurelius wrote to his friend Cincinatus, wherein he toucheth those gentlemen which will take upon them the trade of merchandise against their vocations : divided into four chapters.

[26] The Emperor proceedeth in his letter and declareth what virtues men ought to use and the vices which they ought to eschew.

[27] The Emperor concludeth his letter and persuadeth his friend Cincinatus to despise the vanities of the world and showeth, though a man be never so wise, yet he hath need of another man's counsel.

[28] The author persuadeth princes and great lords to fly covetousness and avarice and to become liberal, which is a virtue seemly for a royal person.

[29] The author persuadeth gentlemen and those that profess arms not to abase themselves by taking upon them any vile offices for gain sake.

B

[30] Of a letter the Emperor wrote to his neighbour Mercurius wherein men may learn the dangers of those which traffic by sea and see the covetousness of them that travel by land.

[31] The Emperor followeth his matter and concludeth his letter rebuking his friend Mercurius for that he took thought for the loss of his goods. He showeth the nature of fortune and the conditions of the covetous man.

[32] That princes and noble men ought to consider the misery of man's nature and that brute beasts are in some points (reason set apart) to be preferred unto man.

[33] The author compareth the misery of man with the liberty of beasts.

[34] The Emperor writeth his letter to Domitius to comfort him being banished for a quarrel betwixt him and another about the running of a horse, very comfortable to all them that have been in prosperity and are now brought into adversity.

[35] That princes and noble men ought to be advocates for widows, fathers of orphans and helpers of all those which are comfortless.

[36] That the troubles, griefs, and sorrows of women are much greater than those of men, wherefor princes and noble men ought to have more compassion upon women than on men.

[37] Of a letter which the Emperor wrote to a Roman lady named Lavinia comforting her for the death of her husband, which is a great consolation for all those that are sorrowful for the decease of their friends.

[38] The Emperor persuadeth widows to put their wills unto the will of God and exhorteth them to live honestly.

[39] That princes and noble men ought to despise Book III the world for that there is nothing in the world but plain deceit.

[40] The Emperor speaketh vehemently against the deceits of the world.

[41] Of a letter which the Emperor Marcus Aurelius wrote to Torquatus to comfort him in his banishment, which is notable for all men to learn the vanities of this world.

[42] The Emperor persuadeth all men by strong and high reasons, not to trust the world nor anything therein.

[43] Princes and noble men ought not to bear with jugglers, jesters, parasites, minstrels, loiterers nor with any such kind of rascals, and of the laws which the Romans made in this behalf.

[44] How some loiterers were punished by the ancients and of these rascals of our time.

[45] Of a letter which the Emperor wrote to a friend of his certifying him that he had banished from Rome the jesters, jugglers, conterfeit fools, parasites, ruffians, minstrels, vagabonds and all other loiterers, a notable letter for such as keep counterfeit fools in their houses.

[46] How the Emperor found the sepulchres of many learned philosophers in Hellespont, whereunto he sent all these loiterers.

[47] The Emperor declareth the cause why these jesters and jugglers were admitted into Rome.

* [48] That princes and noble men ought to remember that they are mortal and must die, where are sundry notable consolations against the fear of death.

[49] Of the death of the Emperor Marcus Aurelius and how there are few friends which dare say the truth unto sick men.

[50] Of the comfortable words which the secretary Pannutius spake to the Emperor, Marcus Aurelius, at the hour of his death.

[51] Pannutius the secretary exhorteth all men willingly to accept death and utterly to forsake the world and his vanity.

[52] The answer of the Emperor Marcus to Pannutius his secretary wherein he declares that he took no thought to forsake the world, but all his sorrow was to leave behind him an unhappy child to inherit the empire.

[53] The Emperor Marcus Aurelius concludeth his matter and showeth that sundry young princes for being vicious have undone themselves and impoverished their realms.

[54] Of the words which the Emperor Marcus Aurelius spake unto his son Commodus, necessary for all noble young gentlemen to understand.

[55] The Emperor Marcus Aurelius, among other wholesome counsel, exhorteth his son to keep wise and sage men about him for to give him counsel in all his affairs.

[56] The Emperor followeth his matter and exhorteth his son unto certain particular things worthy to be engraved in the hearts of men.

[57] The good Marcus Aurelius, Emperor of Rome, endeth his purpose and life and of the last words which he spake to his son Commodus and of the table of counsels which he gave him.

¶ The Table of the Fourth Book

The Epistle to the Reader.

The Prologue.

The Argument.

[1] That it is more necessary for the courtier (abiding in court) to be of lively spirits and audacity than it is for the soldier that goeth to serve in the wars.

[2] Of courtiers brawls and quarrels with the har- bingers for ill lodging.

[3] How the courtier should entreat his host or master of the house where he lyeth.

[4] What the courtier must do to win the prince's favour.

[5] What manners and gestures become the courtier when he speaketh to the prince.

[6] How the courtier should behave himself to know and to visit the noble men and gentlemen that be great with the prince and continuing still in court.

* [7] Of the good countenance and modesty, the courtier should have in behaving himself at the prince or noble man's table in the time of his meal.

* [8] What company the courtier should keep and how he should apparel himself.

[9] Of the wise manner the courtier should have to serve and honour the ladies and gentlewomen and also to satisfy and please the ushers and porters of the king's house.

[10] Of the great pains and troubles the courtier hath that is toiled in suits of laws and how he must suffer and behave himself with the judges.

[11] The author speaketh of the beloved of the court, admonishing them to be patient in their troubles and that they be not partial in the affairs of the common weal.

[12] That the officers and beloved of the court should be very diligent and careful in the despatch of the affairs of the princes and common weal, and in correcting and reforming their servants they should also be very circumspect and advised.

[13] That the dearlings of the court beware they be not proud and high minded, for lightly they never fall, but through this wicked vice.

Book IV   [14] That it is not fit for courtiers to be too covetous if they mean to keep themselves out of many troublesome dangers.

[15] That the favoured of the court should not trust too much to their favour and credit they have, nor to the great prosperity of their life, a worthy chapter and full of good doctrine.

[16] The author admonisheth those that are in favour and great with the prince that they take heed of the deceits of the world and learn to live and die honourably and that they leave the court before age overtakes them.

[17] Of the continency of favoured courtiers, and how they ought to shun the company and conversation of dishonest women and to be careful quickly to despatch all such as sue unto them.

[18] That the nobles and beloved of princes exceed not in superfluous fare and that they be not too sumptuous in their meats. A notable chapter for those that use too much delicacy and superfluity.

[19] That the favoured of princes ought not to be dishonest of their tongue nor envious of their words.

[20] A commendation of truth which professed courtiers ought to embrace and in no respect to be found defective in the contrary, telling one thing for another.

¶ Here beginneth the Table of the letters, translated out of Spanish, which were not in the French copy.

[1] Of a huge monster which was seen in Sicily in the time of Marcus Aurelius.

[2] Of that which chanced unto a neighbour of his in Rome in the time of his Empire.

[3] How Marcus Aurelius, the Emperor, sought the Letters wealth of his people, and how his people loved him.

[4] How at the intercession of many, which the Empress had sent, the Emperor granted his daughter Lucilla licence to sport herself at the feasts.

[5] Of the sharp words which Marcus Aurelius spake to his wife and to his daughters.

[6] The Emperor exhorteth his wife to take away all occasions of the evil from her daughter, wherein is declared the frailty of the tender flesh.

[7] Of the wisdom of Marcus Aurelius in procuring husbands for his daughters.

[8] Of a letter which the Emperor Marcus Aurelius sent to his especial friend to comfort him in his troubles.

[9] A letter sent by the Emperor Marcus Aurelius to Censorius that was so sorrowful for the death of his son, worthy to be read and noted.

[10] A letter sent by Marcus Aurelius, Emperor, to Censorius of the news which at that time was at Rome.

[11] Of a sharp letter full of reprehensions sent by the Emperor Marcus Aurelius to the amorous ladies of Rome, because in his absence they devised a play of him.

[12] A letter which he sent to his lover Bohemia for that she desired so earnestly to go with him to the wars, wherein is to be noted the great folly of young men and the little shame of evil women.

[13] The answer of Bohemia to the Emperor, Marcus Aurelius, wherein is expressed the great malice and little patience of an evil woman.

[14] Of a letter which the Emperor Marcus Aurelius sent to the Lady Macrine, the Roman, of whom (beholding her at the window) he became enamoured, which declareth what force the beauty of a fair woman hath in a weak man.

Letters   [15] Of another letter which the Emperor sent to the Lady Macrine wherein he expresseth the fiery flames which consume soonest the gentle hearts.

[16] Of a letter which the Emperor Marcus Aurelius sent to the beautiful lady of Lybia, wherein he reproveth that love is natural, and that the most part of the philosophers and men have been by love overcome.

¶ The end of the Table.

FROM

'The first booke of the Diall of Princes, with the famous booke of Marcus Aurelius, wherein he entreateth what excellencie is in the Prince, that is a good Christian : and contrarywise, what evils do followe him that is a cruel tyrant.'

How Princes and great Lords in old time were lovers of wise men. [Chap. xliij.]

*   *   *   *   *   *

¶ The lack of a physician may cause danger in man's person, but the lack of a wise man may set discord amongst the people : for where there is any tumult amongst the people, a ripe counsel of a wise man profiteth more than a hundred purgations of rhubarb. Isidorus, in the fourth book of his Etymologies, affirmeth that the Romans were four hundred years without physicians, for Esculapius, the son of Apollo, was the last physician in Greece. And in the temple of the same Esculapius they set up the image of Archabuto, a man very notable in surgery. For the Romans were so beneficious to virtuous persons that to every one that exceeded another in any kind of virtue, they rewarded him with money, they set up a statue of him for memory, or else they made him free in the common wealth. And then when the surgeon Archabuto was become ancient and very rich and when by occasion of great and dangerous wounds he did cut off the arms and legs of

27

certain Romans, they thought him a cruel and unnatural man : wherefore they drove him out of his house, and killed him with stones in the field of Mars. And let no man marvel thereat, for oft times men suffer less harm in enduring the pain than to tarry for the cruel remedies that surgeons apply unto it.

Some men will say, that when Rome was without surgeons, the Romans were discomfited and half lost. To this I will answer that they never had a more prosperous time than in the four hundred years when they were without surgeons : for then was Rome undone, when they received surgeons, for at that time they drove philosophers out of Rome. I do not speak this as a prejudice to any surgeon, for me thinketh that princes cannot be without some among them. For as the flesh is feeble and delicate, so daily needeth it remedies to comfort it. The sage surgeons give us none but good and healthful counsels. For they do not persuade us to any other thing, but that we be sober and continent in eating, drinking, sleeping, travailing, and working, and that in all things we should be temperate.

The end why I speak these things is to persuade princes, prelates, and great lords, that the great diligence they have to seek surgeons, and the sum of money they waste to maintain and content them, they should spend part of that to seek wise men to counsel their persons. For, if men knew what it were to keep a wise man to command in their house, they would give for one only wise man all their goods.

Ye ought to have pity and compassion upon those princes and great lords, which lose so many days in the month and so many hours in the day, in speaking of wars, buildings, weapons, meats, beasts, of huntings, and medicines and often times of other men's doings and of other vain things, not necessary for man's life. And this communication they use with those that are neither virtuous nor wise : the which can neither wisely talk, nor yet answer directly unto that which is asked. Often times it chanceth that a prince at random moveth a matter which they never saw written before, nor with their ears they never heard the like, neither in all their life time they had knowledge thereof, and yet they will seem to give judgement of it (or better to say) obstinately to contend, as if all the days of their life they had studied it : which thing proceedeth of great shame and evil bringing up. For the privy council may speak before their princes, but be they never so privy, with licence or without licence, it is not lawful for them to contend.

Helius Spartianus, in the life of Alexander

Seuerus sayeth, that the Emperor Seuerus
was demanded once by an ambassador of
Greece what thing was most painful to him in
Rome. Whereunto the Emperor answered:
'There is nothing grieveth me more than
when I am merry that my servants should
raise any strife or debate. I am not displeased that matters should be debated, but
this grieveth me when one will obstinately
strive, that hath no ground of that he speaketh. For the man which giveth reason of
that he speaketh cannot be called obstinate.'

Theodosius the Emperor was once demanded what a prince ought to do to be
good, whereunto he answered: 'The virtuous prince when he goeth abroad ought
to have grave and wise men in his company
to discourse with all, when he is at his meat
to have wise men at his board disputing,
and when he withdraweth himself apart to
be reading with wise men : and finally, at
all vacant times, he ought to be found with
sage men counselling. For the knight which
entereth into battle without weapons, is as
hardy as the prince which will govern the
common wealth without the counsel of wise
men.'

FROM

' The second booke of the Diall of Princes,
wherein the Authour treateth howe Princes
and great Lordes should behave themselves
towardes their wyves. And howe they
ought to nourish, and bring up their
children.'

Of the revenge a woman of Greece took of him that had killed her husband, in hope to have her in marriage. [Chap. v.]

¶ Plutarch, in the book he made of the noble and worthy women, declareth a thing worthy of rehearsal and to be had in memory.

¶ In the City of Galatia were two renowned citizens whose names were Sinatus and Sinoris, which were by blood cousins, and in familiarity friends : and for the love of a Greek's daughter, being very noble, beautiful, and exceeding gracious, they both strived to have her in marriage, and for to attain to their desires, they both served her, they both followed her, they both loved her, and for her both of them desired to die. For the dart of love is as a stroke with a clod of earth : the which being thrown amongst a company, doth hurt the one, and blind the others. And as the fatal destinies had ordained it, Sinatus served this Lady called Camma in such sort, that in the end he obtained her in marriage for his lawful wife : which thing when Sinoris perceived, he was

ashamed of his doings, and was also wounded
in his heart. For he lost not only that
which of so long time he had sought, loved,
and served, but also the hope to attain to
that which chiefly in his life he desired.

Sinatus therefore, seeing that his wife
Camma was noble, meek, gracious, fair and
loving, and that in all things she was comely
and well taught, decreed to offer her to the
Goddess Diana, to the end that she would
preserve her from peril, and keep her from
infamy.   Truly we cannot reprove the knight
Sinatus for that he did, nor we ought to note
him for rash in his counsel : for he saw that
his wife was very fair and therefore much
desired. For with great difficulty that is
kept, which of many is desired.

Though Camma was now married, and
that she was in the protection of the Goddess
Diana, yet, notwithstanding, her old friend
Sinoris died for her sake, and by all means
possible he served her, continually he importuned her, daily he followed her, and
hourly he required her. And all this he did
upon certain hope he had, that such diligent
service should suffice to make her change
her sacred mind : and as she had chosen
Sinatus for her husband openly, so he thought
she should take him for her friend secretly.
For many women are as men without taste
through sickness, the which eat more of that

that is hurtful and forbidden than of that which is healthsome and commanded.

Not without a cause Camma was greatly renowned throughout all Galatia for her beauty, and much more among the virtuous esteemed for her honesty. The which evidently in this was seen, that after she was married, Sinoris could never cause her to receive any jewel, or other gift, nor that she would hear him speak any word, nor that she would shew herself in the window, either to him, or to any other, to the end to be seen in the face. For it is not sufficient for Ladies to be pure and good, but also to give no occasion for men to judge (that if they durst) they would be evil.

As it is true indeed that the heart which is entangled with love dare boldly adventure himself in many kind of dangers, to accomplish that which he desired : so Sinoris seeing that with fair words he could not flatter her, nor with any gifts win her, determined to kill Sinatus her husband, upon hope that when she should be widow, he might easily obtain her in matrimony. For he thought, although Camma was not evil, it was not for that she wanted desire to do it, but because she had no commodious place to accomplish it.

And to be short, Sinoris would needs execute and bring to effect his devilish and

damnable intent : so that soon after he
vilely slew his said companion Sinatus,
after whose death the noble Lady Camma
was of Sinoris greatly desired, and by his
parents much importuned that she would
condescend to take and marry him, and that
she would forgive him the death of her
husband Sinatus, which then was buried.
And as she was in all her doings such a
princely woman, she imagined with herself,
that under the pretence of marriage she
might have opportunity to accomplish her
desires : wherefore she answered unto his
parents that she did accept their counsel
and said to Sinoris that she did choose him
for her husband, speaking these words more
for to comfort him than with intent to pardon
him.

And as amongst those of Galatia there
was a custom, that the new married folks
should eat together in one dish and drink
in one cup, the day that the marriage was
celebrated, Camma determined to prepare
a cup with poison, and also a lute, wherewith
she began to play and sing with her proper
voice before the Goddess Diana in this
manner :

> To thee, Dian, whose endless reign doth stretch
> Above the bonds of all the heavenly rout,
> And eke whose aid, with royal hand to reach,
> Chief of all gods, is most proclaimed out :

I swear, and with unspotted faith protest,
That though till now, I have reserved my breath,
For no intent it was, but thus distressed,
With wailful end, to wreak Sinatus death.

And if in mind I had not thus decreed,
Whereto should I my pensive days have spent
With longer dewle [1] : for that forepassed deed
Whose oft record new sorrows still hath bent ?
But oh since him their kindled spite hath slain,
With tender love whom I have weighed so dear :
Since he by fate is reft from fortunes rain,
For whose decay I dreadless perish here :

Since him by whom my only life I led,
Through wretched hands the gaping earth now have,
Ought I by wish to live in any stead
But, closed with him, together in the grave ?
O bright Dian, since senseless him I see,
And makeless I, here to remain alone :
Since he is graved where greedy worms now be,
And I survive, surmounted with my fone [2] :

Since he is pressed with lumps of wretched soil,
And I thus charged with flame of frozen care :
Thou knowest Dian, how hard with restless toil
Of hate abhorring mind, my life I spare.
For how can this unquiet breast reserve
The fainting breath, that strives to draw his last :
Since that even then my dying heart did starve,
When my dead phere [3] in swallowing earth was cast ?

The first black day my husband slept in grave,
By cruel sword my life I thought to spend :
And since a thousand times, I sought to have
A stretched cord, my sorrow's wrath to end.

---

[1] 'dewle' (Fr. *deuil*), mourning.   [2] 'fone' (foen), foes.
[3] 'phere' (fere), comrade.

And if till now to waste my pining days,
I have deferred, by slaughter of my hand,
It was but, lo, a fitter cause to raise
Whereon his sharp revenge might justly stand.

Now since I may in full sufficing wise
Redeem his breath (if wayward will would let),
More deep offence by not revenge [1] might rise
Than Sinoris erst, by guiltless blood, did get.
Thee therefore, mighty Jove, I justly crave,
And eke thy daughter chaste, in thankful sort,
That, lo, the offering, which of myself ye have,
Ye will vouchsafe into your heavenly fort.

Since Sinatus, with soon inflamed eyes,
Amongst the Achaian routes me chiefly viewed,
And eke amidst the prease of Greeks likewise
Chose for his phere, when sweetly he had sued :
Since at my will the froth of wasting wealth
With gladsome mind he trained was to spend :
Since that his youth, which slippeth, lo, by stealth,
To wait on me he freely did commend :

Since he such heaps of ling'ring harms did wast
Aye to content my wanton youthly will,
And that his breath to fade did pass so fast
To glut their thirst, that thus his blood did spill :
Though great the duty be, which that I owe
Unto his graved ghost and cindered mould,
Yet, lo, me seems, my duty well I show,
Performing that my feeble power could.

For since for me untwined was his thread
Of guiltless life, that ought to purchase breath,
Can reason's doom conclude, I ought to dread,
For his decay, to climb the steps of death ?

[1] 'by not revenge' = 'a non le venger' (L'Orloge des Princes, 1550).

In wretched earth, my father graved lies,
My dear mother hath run her race of life,
The pride of love no more can daunt mine eyes,
My wasted goods are shrunk by fortune's strife.

My honour soon eclipsed is by fate,
My young delight is, lo, fordone by chance,
My broken life these passed haps so hate
As can my graved heart no more advance.
　And now remains, to duty with my phere,
No more but refuse, lo, my irksome life,
With willing mind, followed eke with drear,
Which I resign, as fitteth for a wife.

And thou, Sinoris, which Juno's yoke dost crave
To press my corpse, to feed thy liking lust,
The rout of Homer's gods thee grant to have,
Instead of royal feasts, a throne of dust.
　In change of costless robes and rich array
A simple winding sheet they deign thee give,
And eke, instead of honest wedlock's stay,
They sing thy dirge and not vouchsafe thee live.

In place of Hymen's high unfiled bed,
They lay thee up in closure of thy grave :
Instead with precious meats for to be fed,
They make the worms for fitter prey thee have.
　Instead of song, and music's tuned sowne,
They wait on thee with loud lamenting voice :
In change of joyful life and high renown,
Thy cruel death may spread with wretched noise.

For you, great gods, that stalled be on high,
Should not be just, nor yet such titles claim,
Unless this wretch ye ruthless cause to die
That liveth now, to slander of your name.

And thou, Dian, that haunted courts dost shun,
Know'st with what great delight this life I leave,
And, when the race of spending breath is done,
Will pierce the soil that did my phere receive.

And if perchance the paled ghosts despise
Such fatal fine,[1] with grudge of thankless mind,
Yet at the least, the shamefaced living eyes
Shall have a glass, rare wifely gifts to find,
Wherein I will that Lucres' sect shall gaze,
But none that live like Helen's line in blaze.

And when the prayer was ended, that this fair and virtuous Camma made, she drank and gave to drink to Sinoris of this cup of poison, who thought to drink no other but good wine and water : and the case was such, that he died at noonday, and she likewise in the evening after. And truly her death of all Greece with as great sorrow was lamented, as her life of all men was desired.

Princesses and great Ladies may most evidently perceive by the examples herein contained, how honest and honourable it is for them to love and endeavour themselves to be beloved of their husbands : and that not only in their life, but also after their death. For the wife to serve her husband in his life, seemeth ofttimes to proceed of fear : but to love and honour him in his grave, proceedeth of love. Princesses and great Ladies ought not to do that, which

---

[1] 'fine,' end.

many other women of the common people
do, that is to wit, to seek some drinks and
invent some shameful sorceries to be beloved
of their husbands : for albeit it is a great
burden of conscience, and lack of shame in
like manner to use such superstitions, yet
it should be a thing too unjust and very
slanderous, that for to be beloved of their
husbands, they should procure to be hated
of God. Truly to love, to serve, and content
God, it is not hurtful to the woman, for that
she should be the better beloved of her
husband : but yet God hath suffered and
doth permit ofttimes, that the women being
feeble, deformed, poor, and negligent, should
be better beloved of their husbands than
the diligent, fair, and rich. And this is not
for the services they do to their husbands,
but for the good intention they have to
serve and love God, which showeth them
this especial favour : for otherwise God doth
not suffer, that he being with her displeased, she should live with her husband
contented.

If women would take this counsel that I
give them in this case, I will teach them
furthermore a notable enchantment, to obtain the love of their husbands, which is :
that they be quiet, meek, patient, solitary,
and honest, with which five herbs they may
make a confection, the which neither seen

nor tasted of their husbands, shall not only
cause them to be beloved, but also honoured.
For women ought to know that for their
beauty they are desired : but for their virtue
only they are beloved.

II

Of the importunate suit of the Empress Faustine
to the Emperor Marcus Aurelius concern-
ing the key of his closet.   [Chap. xiv.]

¶ We have declared how the Emperor
Marcus Aurelius had his study in the secretest
place of all the palace, and how that he himself did keep the key. It is to be under-
standed that he would never let his wife, his
children, nor any other of his familiar friends
come into it, for he said : ' I had rather
suffer that they should take from me my
treasures than that any man should turn
the leaves of my books.'

It chanced that one day the Empress
Faustine, being great with child, importuned
the Emperor much by all the means she
could that he would be so favourable unto
her as to give her the key of his study and it
is no marvel : for naturally women despise
that which is given them and lust for that
that is denied them. Faustine instantly
besought him, not once, but many times,

not only with fair words, but with abundant tears, alleging unto him these reasons.

' I have required thee sundry times that thou wouldst give me the key of thy chamber and thou hast, by jesting, made frustrate my request, the which thou (my lord) oughtest not to have done, considering that I am with child, for often times it chanceth, that that wherefore the husband rejoiceth this day, to-morrow he doth lament. Thou oughtest to remember that I am that Faustine the renowned, the which in thy eyes am the fairest, and of thy tongue have been most commended, of thy person I was best beloved, and of thy heart I am most desired. Then since it is true, that thou hast me so deeply in heart why then doubtest thou to show me the writings of thy study ? Thou dost communicate with me the secrets of the Empire, and thou hidest from me the books of thy study. Thou hast given me thy tender heart of flesh and now thou deniest me the hard key of the room. Now, I must needs think, that thy love was feigned and thy words were double, and that thy thoughts were others than they seemed. For if they had been otherwise, it had been impossible thou shouldst have denied me the key of that I do ask thee, for where love is unfeigned, though the request be merrily asked, yet it is willingly granted.

' It is a common custom, that you men
use to deceive us simple women, you present
great gifts, you give many fair words, you
make us fair promises, you say you will do
marvels, but in the end you do nothing but
deceive us : for we are persecuted more of
you than of any others.   When men, in such
wise, importune the women, if the women
had power to deny and withstand, we should
in short space bring ye under the yoke, and
lead you by the noses : but when we suffer
ourselves to be overcome, then you begin
to forsake us, and despise us.   Let me, therefore (my lord), see thy chamber, consider I
am with child, and that I die unless I see it.
If thou dost not do me pleasure, yet do it
at the least because I may no more importune
thee.   For, if I come in danger through this
my longing, I shall but lose my life : but thou
shalt lose the child that should be born, and
the mother also that ought to bear it.   I
know not why thou shouldst put thy noble
heart into such a dangerous fortune, whereby
both thou and I at one tine should perish :
I in dying so young, and thou in losing so
loving a wife.

¶ ' By the immortal gods I do beseech
thee, and by the mother Berecinthia I conjure thee, that thou give me the key, or
that thou let me enter into the study : and
stick not with me, thy wife, in this my

small request, but change thy opinion : for all that which without consideration is ordained, by importunate suit may be revoked. We see daily that men by reading in books love their children, but I never saw heart of man fall in such sort that by reading and looking in books he should despise his children : for in the end books are by the words of others made : but children are with their own proper blood begotten. Before that anything of wisdom is begun, they always regard the inconveniences that may follow. Therefore if thou wilt not give me this key, and that thou art determined to be stubborn still in thy will, thou shalt lose thy Faustine, thou shalt lose so loving a wife, thou shalt lose the creature wherewith she is big, thou shalt lose the authority of thy palace, thou shalt give occasion to all Rome to speak of thy wickedness and this grief shall never depart from thy heart : for that heart shall never be comforted, that knoweth that he only is the occasion of his own grief. If the gods do suffer it by their secret judgment, and if my woeful mishaps deserve it, and if thou (my lord) desirest it for no other cause, but even to do after thy will, for denying me this key, I should die : I would willingly die. But of that I think thou wilt repent : for it chanceth oftentimes to wise men, that when remedy is gone, the repentance cometh suddenly : and then it is too late (as they say) to shut the stable door when the steed is stolen.

¶ 'I marvel much at thee, my lord, why thou shouldst show thyself so froward in this case, since thou knowest that all the time we have been togethers, thy will and mine hath alway been one : if thou wilt not give me thy key, for that I am thy well beloved Faustine, if thou wilt not let me have it, since I am thy dear beloved wife, if thou wilt not give it me for that I am great with child, I beseech thee give it me in virtue of the ancient law. For thou knowest it is an inviolate law among the Romans that a man cannot deny his wife with child her desires. I have seen sundry times with mine eyes many women sue their husbands at the law in this behalf : and thou, lord, commandeth that a man should not break the privileges of women.

¶ 'Then, if this thing be true (as it is true indeed) why wilt thou that the laws of strange children should be kept and that they should be broken to thine own children ? Speaking according to the reverence that I owe unto thee, though thou wouldest, I will not, though thou doest it, I will not agree thereunto, and though thou doeth command it, in this case I will not obey thee. For if the husband do not accept the just request of his wife, the wife is not bound to obey the unjust commandment of her husband. You husbands desire that your wives should serve you, you desire that your wives should obey you in all, and ye will condescend to nothing that they desire. You men say, that we women have no certainty in our love, but indeed you have no love at all. For by this it appeareth that your love is feigned, in that it no longer continueth when your desires are satisfied.

¶ 'You say, furthermore, that the women are suspicious, and that is true in you all men may see, and not in us : for none other cause there are so many evil married in Rome, but because their husbands have of them such evil opinions. There is a great difference between suspicion of the woman and the jealousy of the man : for if a man will understand the suspicion of the woman, it is no other thing, but to show to her husband that she loveth him with all her heart. For the innocent women know no others, desire no others, but their husbands only, and they would that their husbands should know no others, nor search for any others, nor love any others, nor will any others, but them only : for the heart that is bent to love one only, would not that into that house should enter any other.

¶ 'But you men know so many means, and use so many subtleties, that you praise yourselves for to offend them, you vaunt yourselves to deceive them, and that it is true, a man can in nothing so much show his nobleness as to sustain and favour a courtesan.

¶ 'The husbands please their wives speaking unto them some merry words, and immediately their backs being turned, to another they give both their bodies and their goods. I swear unto thee (my lord) that if women had the liberty and authority over men, as men have over women, they should find more malice, deceitfulness and craft, by them committed in one day than they should find in the women all the days of their life.

'You men say that women are evil speakers. It is true indeed that your tongues are none other but the stings of serpents : for ye do condemn the good men, and defame the Roman women. And think not (if you speak evil of other women) to excuse your own : for the man that by his tongue dishonoureth strange women doth not so much evil as he doeth by defaming his own wife by suspicion. For the husband that suspecteth his wife, giveth all men licence to account her for nought. Since we women go little out of the house, we travel not far, and since we see few things, though we would, we cannot be evil tongued : but you men hear much, you see much, you know much, you wander abroad much, and continually you murmur. All the evil that we seely women can do, is to listen to our friends when they are vexed, to chide our servants when they are negligent, to envy our neighbours if they be fair and to curse those that do us injury : finally, though we speak evil, we cannot murmur, but at those that dwell in the same street where we dwell.

' But you men defame your wives by suspicion, you dishonour your neighbours in your words, you speak against strangers with cruelty, you neither keep faith nor promise to your wives, you show yourselves extreme against your enemies, you murmur both at those that be present and also at them that be absent : finally, on the one part you are so double, and on the other part you are so unthankful, that to those whom you desire you make fair promises, and those whose bodies you have enjoyed you little esteem. I confess that the woman is not so good as she ought to be, and that it is necessary that she should be kept in the house, and so she shall lead a good life, and being of good life she shall have good renown, and, having good renown, she shall be well willed : but if perchance any of those do want in her, yet for all that she ought not

D

to be rejected of her husband. For the frailness that men find in women is but little : but the evils that women taste in men is very great.

'I have talked longer than I thought, and have said more boldly than I ought, but pardon me (my lord) for mine intention was not to vex thee, but to persuade thee. For in the end he is a fool that taketh that for injury, which passeth between the man and the wife in secret. I stick always to my first point, and if it need, once again I require thee that thou wilt give me the key of thy study : and if thou do otherwise (as thou mayest) thou shalt do such a thing as thou oughtest not to do. I am not angry so much for that thou doest, as for the occasion thou givest me.

¶ 'Therefore to avoid the peril of my delivery, and to take from me all suspicion, I pray thee (my lord) deliver me the key of thy study : for otherwise I cannot be per-suaded in my heart, but that you have a woman locked in your study. For men that in their youth have been unconstant, though the apparel that they have be not worn, yet notwithstanding, they desire to have new. Therefore, once again, to preserve me from peril in my delivery, and to lighten my heart of this thought, it shall be well done that you let me enter into your study.'

The answer of the Emperor to Faustine concerning her demand of the key of the study. [Chap. xv.]

¶ The Emperor hearing the words of Faustine, and seeing that she spake them so earnestly that she bathed her woeful words with bitter tears, determined also to answer her as earnestly, and said unto her these words.

' Wife Faustine, thou hast told me all that thou wouldest, and I have heard all thy complaint. Therefore I desire thee now to have as much patience to hear my answer : as I have had pain to hear thy demand. And prepare thy ears to hear my words : as I have listened mine to hear thy folly. For in like matter, when the tongue doth apply itself to speak any word, the ears ought immediately to prepare them to hear it, for to make answer. For this is most sure, that he that speaketh what he would shall hear what he would not.

' Before I tell thee what thou art, and what thou oughtest to be, I would first tell thee what I am, and what I ought to be. For I will thou understand, Faustine, that I am so evil that that the which mine enemies do report of me, is but a trifle in respect of that which my familiars and friends would

say if they knew me.   To the end the prince
be good, he ought not to be covetous of
tributes, neither proud in commandments,
nor unthankful of services, nor to be forgetful
of the temples : he ought not to be deaf to
hear griefs, complaints, and quarrels, nor
cruel to orphans, nor yet negligent in affairs.
And the man that shall want these vices
shall be both beloved of men, and favoured
of the gods.   I confess first of all that I have
been covetous.   For indeed those which with
troubles annoy princes least, and with
money serve them most, are of all other men
beloved best.

¶ 'Secondarily, I confess that I am proud :
for there is no prince at this day in the world
so brought under, but when fortune is most
lowest he hath his heart very haughty.

¶ 'Thirdly, I confess that I am unthankful :
for amongst us that are princes, the services
that they do unto us are great, and the
rewards that we give unto them are little.

¶ 'Fourthly, I do confess that I am an
evil founder of temples : for amongst us
princes we do not sacrifice unto the gods
very oft, unless it be when we see ourselves
to be environed with enemies.

¶ 'Fifthly, I confess that I am negligent
to hear the plaints of the oppressed : for the
flatterers have towards their princes more
easy audience by their flattery, than the

poor, pleading to declare their complaints by truth.

¶ 'Sixthly, I confess that I am careless for the orphans: for in the courts and palaces of princes the rich and mighty are most familiar, but the miserable and poor orphans are scarcely heard.

¶ 'Seventhly, I confess that I am negligent in despatching poor men's causes: for princes ofttimes, not providing in time for their affairs, many great perils ensueth to their Realms.

¶ 'Mark here, Faustine, how I have told thee what (according to reason) I ought to be, and what according to the sensuality I am: and marvel not though I confess mine error. For the man that acknowledgeth his faults giveth hope of amendment. Let us now come to talk of thee, and, by that I have spoken of me, thou mayst judge of thyself. For we men are so evil conditioned, that we behold the uttermost the offences of another, but we will not hear the faults of ourselves. It is a true thing my wife Faustine, that when a woman is merry, she always speaks more with her tongue than she knoweth in her heart. For women light of tongue speak many things in company, the which they do lament after when they are alone. All the contrary cometh to woeful men, for they do not speak the half of their griefs:

because their heavy and woeful hearts commandeth their eyes to weep, and their
tongues to be silent. Vain and foolish men,
by vain and foolish words do publish their
vain and light pleasures : and the wise men
by wise words do dissemble their grievous
sorrows. For though they feel the troubles
of this life, they dissemble them as men.
Amongst the sages he is most wisest that
presumeth to know least : and amongst the
simple he is most ignorant that thinketh to
know most. For if there be found one that
knoweth much : yet always there is found
another that knoweth more. This is one
difference whereby the wise men are known
from those that be simple, that is to say that,
the wise man to one that asketh him a question answereth slowly and gravely, and the
simple man, though he be not asked, answereth quick and lightly. For in the house
where nobleness and wisdom are, they give
riches without measure, but they give words
by ounces.

'I have told thee all this, Faustine, because
thy words have wounded me in such sort,
thy tears in such wise have compelled me,
and thy vain judgements have wearied me
so much, that I cannot say what I would,
nor I think thou canst perceive what I say.
Those which wrote of marriage wrote many
things : but they wrote not so many troubles

in all their books, as one woman causeth her husband to feel in one day.

¶ 'The ancients spake well when they reasoned of marriages : for at all times when they talked of marriage, at the beginning they put these words : " Onus Matrimonii." That is to say, the yoke of marriage. For truly if the man be not well married, all the troubles that may happen unto him in all the times of his life, are but small in respect to be matched one day with an evil wife.

¶ 'Dost thou think, Faustine, that it is a small trouble for the husband to suffer the brawlings of his wife ? To endure her vain words, to bear with her fond words ? To give her what she requireth ? To seek that she desireth ? And to dissemble with all their vanities ? Truly, it is so unpatient a trouble that I would not desire any greater revengement of my enemy than to see him married with a brawling wife.

¶ 'If the husband be proud, you do humble him : for there is no proud man, whatsoever he be, but a fierce woman will make him stoop. If the husband be foolish you restore him his senses again : for there is no greater wisdom in the world, than to know how to endure a brawling woman. If the husband be wild, you make him tame : for the time is so much that you occupy in brawling, that he can have no time to speak.

If the husband be slow, you make him run : for he desireth so much your contentation in heart, that the woeful man cannot eat in quiet, nor sleep in rest. If the husband be a great talker, in short space you make him dumb : for the flouts and mocks that you give him at every word are so many in number, that he hath none other remedy but to refrain his tongue. If the husband be suspicious, you make him change his mind : for the trifles that you ask at every hour are such, and so many, and you therewith so self-willed, that he dare not tell what he seeth in his own house. If the husband be a wanderer abroad, you make him forthwith to be a bider at home : for you look so ill to the house and goods, that he findeth no other remedy but to be always at home. If the husband be vicious, you restrain him immediately : for you burden his heart with so many thoughts, that his body hath no delight to use any pleasures. Finally I say, that if the husband be peaceable, within short space you make him unquiet : for your pains are such, so many, and so continual, that there is no heart can wholly dissemble them, nor tongue that can utterly keep them secret.

' Naturally women have in all things the spirit of contradiction, for so much as if the husbands will speak, they will hold their peace. If he go forth, they will tarry at home. If he will laugh, they will weep. If he will take pleasure, they will vex him. If he be sorrowful, they will be merry. If he desire peace, they would have war. If he would eat, they will fast. If he would fast, they would eat. If he would sleep, they will watch : and if thou wilt watch, they will sleep. Finally I say, that they are of so evil a condition, that they love all that we despise : and despise all that we love.

'In mine opinion, the men that are wise, and will obtain that which they desire of their wives, let them not demand of them that which they would obtain, if they will come to their desire. For to them which are diseased, the letting of blood is most profitable, when the vein in the contrary side is opened. It is no other thing to be let blood in the contrary side, but to ask of the woman with his mouth the contrary of that which he desireth with his heart : for otherwise neither by fair words of his mouth, nor by the bitter tears of his eyes, he shall ever obtain that which his heart desireth.

'I confess, Faustine, it is a pleasant sport to behold the young babes, and thou canst not deny me, but it is a cruel torment to endure the importunities of their mothers. Children now and then minister unto us occasions of pleasures : but you that are

their mothers never do anything, but that
which turneth us to trouble.

' It is much pleasure to the husband when
he cometh home to find the house clean
swept, to find the table covered, and to find
the meat ready dressed : this is to be under-
standed if all other things be well. But
what shall we say when he seeth the contrary : and that he findeth his children
weeping, his neighbours offended, his servants
troubled, and above all, when he findeth his
wife brawling ? Truly it is better to the
woeful husband to go his way fasting than to
tarry and eat at home with brawling. I
durst take upon me to cause that all married
men would be content to forbear all the
pleasures of the children, with condition
that they might be free from the annoyance
of the mothers : for in the end the pleasures
of the children endeth quickly with laughter,
but the griefs of the mothers endureth all
their life with sorrow.

' I have seen one thing in Rome, wherein
I was never deceived, which is that though
men commit great offences in this world,
yet God always defers the punishment thereof
until another : but if for any woman's
pleasure we commit any fault, God permitteth that, by the same woman, in this
world we shall suffer the pain. There is no
crueller enemy to man, nor more trouble-

some to live withal, than the woman is that he keepeth in his house : for if he suffer her once to have her own will then let him be assured never after to bring her unto obedience. The young men of Rome follow the ladies of Capua, but they may well repent them : for there was never man that haunted of any long time the company of women, but in the end to their procurement, either by death or with infamy, he was defaced. For the Gods esteem that honour above all things, and as they suffer the wickedness of the evil men, so we see the sharp punishments that they ordain for them.

' I am well assured, Faustine, of one thing, and I do not speak it by hearsay but because continually I have proved it, and it is : that the husband which condescendeth to all that the wife desireth, causeth his wife to do nothing of that her husband commandeth. For there is nothing that keepeth a woman more under obedience to her husband, than when oftentimes he denieth with sharp words her unlawful requests. In my opinion it is much cruelty of the barbarous, to keep (as they do) their wives like slaves : but it is much more folly of the Romans, to keep them (as they do) like Ladies. The flesh ought not to be so lean that it be in eating dry, nor yet so fat that there be no lean : but it would participate both of the fat and of the lean, to the intent it might give the more nourishment. I mean, that the man of understanding ought not to keep his wife so short, that she should seem to be his servant, nor yet to give her so much liberty, that she becometh his mistress. For the husband that suffereth his wife to command more than she ought, is the cause why he himself afterwards is not esteemed as he should be.

'Behold, Faustine, you women are in all things so extreme, that for a little favour you wax proud : and for a little displeasure you become great enemies. There is no woman that willingly can suffer to have any superior, nor yet scarcely can endure to have any equal : for we see that you love not the highest, nor desire to be loved by the lowest. For where as the lovers be not equal, there their love cannot be perfect. I know well, Faustine, that thou dost not understand me, therefore hearken what I do tell thee, more than thou thinkest, and more than thou wouldest. Oh what and how many women have I seen in Rome, the which though they had two thousand pound of rent in their houses, yet they had three thousand follies in their heads : and the worst of all is that oft times her husband dieth, and she loseth her rent, yet for all that ceaseth not her folly.

'Now listen, Faustine, and I will tell thee

more. All women will speak, and they will that others be silent. All will command, and will not that they be commanded. All will have liberty, and they will that all be captives to them. All will govern, and will not be governed. Finally they all in this one thing agree, and that is that they will cherish them that they love, and revenge them of those that they hate. Of that which before is said it may be gathered, that they make fools and slaves of the young and vain men which follow them : and persecute the wise men, as enemies that fly them. For in the end whereas they love us most, their love may be measured : but whereas they hate us least, their hate exceedeth reason.

' In the Annals of Pompeius I remember I have read, and do note one thing worthy of knowledge, that when Pompeius the Great passed first into Asia, as by chance he came by the mountains of Rypheos, he found in those places a barbarous nation that lived in the sharp mountains as wild beasts : and do not marvel that I do call them beastly, that live in those mountains. For as the sheep and cows that feed on the fine grass have their wool soft and fine, so the men which are brought up in the sharp and wild mountains, use themselves after a rude behaviour. These barbarians had therefore a law among them, that every neighbour had

in those mountains two caves : for the sharpness of the hills permitted not that they
should have any houses. Therefore in one
cave the husbands, the sons, and the servants
were: and in the other, his wife, his daughters,
and his handmaids abode : they did eat
together twice in the week, they slept togethers other twice in the week, and all the
residue of the time they were separate the
one from the other. The great Pompeius
asked them what the cause was why they
lived so, since it was so that in all the world
there was never seen nor read such extreme
law, nor so strange a custom. The history
sayeth in that place, that an ancient man
answered him, saying, " Behold Pompeius,
that the Gods have given short life unto us
that be present, in respect of that which he
gave to our fathers that are past : and since
we live but forty or fifty years at the uttermost we desire to enjoy those days in peace :
for the life is so short and our troubles so
long, that we have small time to rejoice in
peace after we return from the wars. It is
true that amongst you Romans, which enjoy
pleasure and riches, life seemeth too short :
but unto us that have toil with poverty, life
seemeth too long. For throughout all the
year we never keep such solemn feasts, as
when one passeth out of his life. Consider,
Pompeius, that if men lived many years,

there should be time to laugh and weep, to be good and to be evil, to be poor and to be rich, to be merry and sad, to live in peace and war : but why will men seek contention in their life, since it is so short. In keeping with us (as you do) our own wives, in living we should die, for the nights should pass in hearing their complaints, and the days in suffering their brawlings, but keeping them as we do, we see not their heavy countenance, we hear not the crying of our children, we hear not their grievous complaints, nor listen unto their sorrowful words, neither we are troubled with their importunate suits, and yet the children are nourished in peace, and the father followeth the war : so that they are well, and we are better." This was the answer that this old man gave at the request of the great Pompeius. Truly, Faustine, I say that though we call the Messagetes Barbarous, in this case they know more than the Latins. For he that is free from a brawling woman, hath escaped no small pestilence.

' I ask thee now, Faustine, since those barbarous could not agree, nor would not have their wives with them in those sharp mountains, how shall we other agree, and please you that live in these pleasures in Rome ? One thing I will tell thee, Faustine, and I beseech the gods that thou mayest understand it, which is : if the beastly motions of the flesh did not force men to will, and also to desire women, I doubt whether there should be any women in the world beloved or suffered. For though nature giveth them gifts worthy to be beloved : yet they through their small discretion cause themselves to be hated. If the gods had made this love voluntary, as they made it natural, so that we might have loved as we would and left again at our pleasure, that man ought worthily to have been punished which would, for the love of any woman, put his life in danger. The gods have kept this great secret unto themselves, and the misery that they gave unto men is very great : since that unto so weak flesh he gave so strong a heart, the which doth procure that which doth us harm and followeth that which we ought to abhor. This is another secret, that all men know when they offend, but I see no man that seeketh amendment : for I hear all men complain of the flesh, and yet I see all like butchers follow the flesh : and when it can do least good, then it is most greedy.

' I envy not the gods living nor the men that be dead, save only for two things, which be these. First I envy the gods, because they live without fear of the malicious. Secondarily, I envy the dead for they live

without need of women. For women are
so corrupt, that they corrupt all : and they
be such mortal plagues, that both flesh and
heart by them are brought to end. O Faustine, the love of the flesh is so natural to the
flesh, that when from you the body flieth in
sport, we then leave our hearts engaged to
you in earnest. And though reason as
reason putteth desire to flight, yet the flesh
as flesh yieldeth itself as prisoner.'

*The Emperor following his matter admonisheth
men of the great dangers which ensue unto
them by excessive haunting the company
of women. And reciteth certain rules for
married men which (if they observe) may
cause them to live in peace with their wives.*
[Chap. xvi.]

¶ ' I remember that in my youth, as I was
of flesh, I trembled for fear of the flesh, with
mind never to return again, and I do confess
that oft times I revolved in my heart many
holy and chaste meditations : but yet notwithstanding I gave my body immediately
to sundry filthy vices. It is a natural thing,
that when man hath committed any vice,
forthwith he repenteth him of his deed : and
so again after his new repentance, he turneth
to his old vices. For during the time that
we live in the house of this frail flesh, Sensual-

ity beareth so great a rule that she will not suffer reason to enter in at the gate.

' There is no man in Rome (if a man doth ask him) but will marvel to declare with this tongue the thoughts that he hath had in his heart, in especially to be chaste, to be true, to be patient, and to be virtuous : and per-adventure ye talk with those that somewhat communicate with them, and let a man enquire of his neighbour, they shall find that he is a deceiver, a liar, and a blasphemer. Finally, they deceive men by their fair words, and offend the gods by their evil works.

' It profiteth little to blaze virtues with words, if the hand be negligent to work them in deed : for a man is not called just, only desiring to be good in name, but for to labour to be virtuous in works. The traitorous world in no one thing beguileth worldlings so much as by feeding them with vain hope, saying that they shall have time enough to be virtuous : so that these blind men, when they are once deeply rooted in vices and while they hope for this life of amendment, then suddenly assaulteth them the dreadful dart of death. Oh, how many have promised unto men and vowed unto the gods and deter-mined with themselves that before so many days they would begin to be virtuous : whom in short space after we have seen to engage themselves to the hungry worms of the earth.

The gods will that we be virtuous: and, for the contrary, the world and the flesh willeth that we be vicious. Methinketh that it is better to obey the gods, than to do that the world and the flesh desireth : for the praise of virtue is honour, and the pain of vice is infamy. If thou dost consider, Faustine, thou shalt see that the gods are, on the one part, which procureth us to virtues : and, on the other part, is the world and the flesh, which enticeth us unto vices. My opinion is we should say unto the gods that we desire to be virtuous and that we should say to the world and the flesh, that from henceforth we will give ourselves no more to be vicious. We ought in such case to satisfy the gods with works, and to entertain the world and the flesh with words : that we employ so much time in leading a good life, that we have no time vacant to speak an idle word.

' I let thee wit, Faustine, that all that I have told thee I have spoken it against myself : for always from my youth I had a good mind, and yet, for all that, I have been overthrown with vices. Oh, how many times in my youth I knew women, I accompanied with women, I talked with women, and believed women, the which in the end have deceived me, misused me and defamed me. At the last I withdrew myself and forsook them, but I do confess that if reason kept me from their houses ten days, sensuality kept me with them ten weeks. O cruel gods, O wicked world, O frail flesh, tell me what it meaneth that reason lendeth me voluntarily to virtues, and that sensuality against my will draweth me unto vices.

'Dost thou not think, Faustine, that I consider what a great good it is for to be good, and what an evil it is to be evil? But what shall I do, woeful man, since at this day there is not so cruel a scourge of my honour, nor so great an enemy of my renown, as mine own flesh is, the which against me doth make such cruel wars. Wherefore, I beseech the immortal gods, since my being here is against my will, that they do defend me in this so cruel war. The frail flesh is somewhat to blame, but much more is the foolish and light woman in fault. For if men were certain that women were chaste, shamefaced, and solitary, they would not dispose their hearts, their bodies, nor bend their bows to shoot at their butts: they would not consume their time to follow them, lose their goods to serve them, neither would they suffer so many shames to slander them. For where the heart hath no hope to obtain, there he will give over his suit.

'But what shall we do now, Faustine, (I pray thee tell me) since thou knowest better than I, that the shame of the Roman women

is now gone, and the women of Italy are so
dissolute, that though men do not regard
them, yet they do entice them. If men fly
they call them : if men go back, they ap-
proach : if men are sad, they make them
merry : if men are silent, they force them to
speak : and finally men begin the love in
sport, and they temper it in such sort, that
they turn it all into earnest.

' I let thee wit, Faustine, that the means
whereby nature worketh in man is very
strange, but the shame which the gods put
in women is more marvellous. And if it be
true (as it is true indeed), that the men do
lose the sting of the flesh, and the women do
not lose the shame of the visage, I think it
is impossible that there should be a chaste
or virtuous woman in Rome. For there is
no common wealth more undone, than that
where the women have lost their shame.
O women, what reason have they which fly
from you, which are weary of you, which
forsake you, which forget you, which make
themselves strangers, and furthermore which
are dead and buried. For the hungry worms
gnaw in the grave only the frail and slimy
flesh of the dead : but you women destroy
the goods, honour, and life of the living.
Oh, if the noble hearts knew what evil doth
follow them, for dallying with women: I
swear unto them that they would not serve

them continually as they do serve them : but also they would have no lust nor desire to behold them.

'What wilt thou I say any more to thee, Faustine, but that some scape out of your hands for effeminate and slandered, others hurt by your tongues, others persecuted with your works, others deceived with your countenances, others despised through your hatred, others desperate through your inconstancy, others condemned by your light judgments, others troubled through your unkindness, finally those that escape best are of your hearts abhorred, and through your folly destroyed. Then since the man knoweth that he must pass all those dangers, I cannot tell what fool he is that will either love or serve you. For the brute beast that once hath felt the sharp teeth of the dog, will unwillingly ever after come near unto the stake.

'Oh, unto what perils doth he offer himself which continually doth haunt the company of women. For as much as if he love them not, they despise him and take him for a fool. If he doth love them, they account him for light. If he forsake them, they esteem him for nobody. If he follow them, he is accounted lost. If he serve them, they do not regard him. If he do not serve them, they despise him. If he will have them, they will not. If he will not, they persecute him. If he do advance himself forth, they call him importunate. If he fly, they say he is coward, if he speak, they say he is a bragger. If he holdeth peace, they say he is a dissard.[1] If he laugh, they say he is a fool. If he laugh not, they say he is solemn. If he giveth them anything, they say it is little worth : and he that giveth them nothing, he is a pinchpurse. Finally he that haunteth them, is by them slandered : and he that doth not frequent them, is esteemed less than a man.

' These things so seen, so heard, and so known, what shall the poor and miserable man do, in especially if he be a man of understanding ? For though he would absent himself from women, the flesh doth not give him licence : and though he would follow women, wisdom will not condescend. Some men think in all their thoughts that by services and pleasures they may content women : but I let them know, if they know it not, that the woman is never contented though man doth what he can as maid, and that he do all that he ought to do as a husband : though he taketh pains for her sake above his force, and though with the sweat of his brows he relieveth her need : though every hour he putteth himself in danger, yet in the end, she will give him no thanks : but

---

[1] 'dissard,' fool (O.E. *dysig*).

will say that he loveth another, and that he doth but that to please and satisfy her.

'It is a long time since I desired to tell thee this, Faustine, but I have deferred it until this present hour, hoping thou wouldst not give occasion to tell it thee. For among wise men those words ought chiefly to be esteemed which fitly to the purpose are declared.

'I remember that it is five years since Anthonius Pius (thy father) chose me to be his son-in-law, and that thou chosest me for thy husband, and I thee for my wife: all the which things were done, my woeful adventures permitting it, and Adrian my lord commanding it. The good Anthonius Pius gave his only daughter in marriage unto me, and gave me likewise his noble empire with great treasures: he gave me also the gardens of Vulcanali to pass the time therein. But I think that on both sides we were deceived, he in choosing me for his son-in-law, and I in taking thee for my wife. O Faustine, thy father and my father-in-law was called Anthonius Pius, because to all he was merciful, save only to me to whom he was most cruel: for with a little flesh he gave me many bones. And I confess the truth unto thee that now I have no more teeth to bite, nor heat in my stomach to digest: and the worst of all is, that many times I have thought to rage on myself. I will tell thee one word, though it doth displease me, which is, that for thy beauty thou art desired of many : and for thy evil conditions, thou art despised of all. For the fair women are like unto the golden pills : the which in sight are very pleasant and in eating very noisome.

' Thou knoweth well, Faustine, and I also, that we saw on a day Drusio and Braxille his wife, which were our neighbours, and as they were brawling together I spake unto Drusio such words : " What meaneth this, Lord Drusio, that being now the feast of Berecinthia, and being as we are adjoining to her house, and present before so honourable assembly, and furthermore thy wife being so fair as she is, how it is possible there should be any strife between you ? Men which are married to deformed persons, to the end that they might kill them quickly, should always fall out with their wives : but those that are married to fair women, they ought always to live together in joy and pleasure, to the end they may live long. For when a fair woman dieth, though she hath lived a hundred years, yet she dieth too soon : and though a deformed woman liveth a small time, yet notwithstanding, she dieth too late." Drusio as a man being vexed, lifting up his eyes unto the heavens, fetching a grievous sigh from the bottom of his heart, said these words : " The mother Berecinthia pardon me, and her holy house also, and all the company besides forgive me, for by the immortal gods I swear unto thee, that I had rather had been married with a Moor of Calde that is so foul, than being married as I am with a Roman being very fair : for she is not so fair and white as my life is woeful and black." Thou knowest well, Faustine, that when Drusio spake these words, I did wipe the tears from his eyes, and I gave him a word in his ear that he should proceed no further in this matter : for such women ought to be chastened in secret, and afterwards to be honoured openly.

'Oh thou art unfortunate, Faustine, and the gods have evil divided with thee, giving thee beauty and riches to undo thyself : and denying thee the best, which is wisdom and good conditions to keep thy honour. Oh what evil luck cometh unto a man, when God sendeth him a fair daughter, unless furthermore the gods do permit that she be sage and honest, for the woman which is young, foolish, and fair destroyeth the common wealth and defameth all her parentage.

'I say unto thee again, Faustine, that the gods were very cruel against thee, since they swallow thee up by the gulfs, where all the

evil perisheth : and took from thee all the
sails and oars whereby the good do escape.
I remained thirty-eight years unmarried,
and these six years only which I have been
married, me thinketh I have passed six
hundred years of my life : for nothing can
be called a torment, but the evil that man
doth suffer that is evil married. I will ensure thee of one thing, Faustine, that if I had
known before, which now I know, and that
I had felt that which now I feel, though the
gods had commanded me and the Emperor
Adrian my Lord had desired me, I had not
changed my poverty for thy riches, neither
my rest for thy Empire : but since it is fallen
to thine and mine evil fortune, I am contented to speak little and to suffer much. I
have so much dissembled with thee, Faustine, that I can no more : but I confess unto
thee, that no husband doth suffer his wife
so much, but that he is bound to suffer her
more, considering that he is a man, and that
she is a woman. For the man which willingly goeth into the briars must think before
to endure the pricks. The woman is too
bold that doth contend with her husband :
but the husband is more fool which openly
quarreleth with his wife. For if she be good,
he ought to favour her to the end she may
be better : if she be unhappy, he ought to
suffer her to the end she be not worse.

Truly when the woman thinketh that her husband taketh her for evil, it is a great occasion to make her to be worse, for women are so ambitious that those which commonly are evil will make us believe that they are better than others.

' Believe me, Faustine, that if the fear of the gods be infamy of the person, and the speech of men do not restrain the woman, all the chastisements of the world will not make her restrain from vice : for all things suffereth chastisement and correction, the woman only except, the which must be won by entreaty. The heart of man is very noble, and that of the woman very delicate : because for a little good he will give a great reward, and for a great offence, he will give no punishment. Before the wise man marrieth, let him beware what he doth : and when he shall determine to take the company of a woman, he ought to be like unto him that entereth into the war, that determineth to himself to suffer all that may happen, be it good or evil. I do not call that life a war without a cause, which the evil married man leadeth in his house : for women do more hurt with their tongues than the enemies do with their swords. It is a great simplicity for a wise man to make account, or esteem the simplicity of his wife at every time, for if they would mark, and take heed to that

which their wife doth, or saith, I let them
know that they shall never come to an end.

' O Faustine, if the Roman woman would
always one thing, that they would procure
one thing, that they would be resolved in
one thing, though it were to our great charges
we should have pleasure to condescend unto
their desires : but what shall we do, since
that which now pleaseth you a while after
displeaseth you, that which you ask for in
the morning ye will not have at noon, that
which you enjoy at noon days will trouble
you in the night, that which in the night
you love ye care not for in the morning,
that which yesterday ye greatly esteemed
to-day ye as much despise. If ye desired to
see a thing the last year, this year ye will
not hear talk of it : that which before made
you rejoice doth now make you be sad, that
which ye were wont and ought to lament, at
the self same thing a man seeth you laugh.
Finally, ye women are as children, which are
appeased with an apple, and casteth the
gold to the earth not wanting it.

' I have divers times thought with myself,
if I could say or write any good rule, in
keeping the which I might teach men to be
quiet in their house. And by my count I
find (having experimented it also with thee,
Faustine,) that it is impossible to give a rule
to married men : and if a man could give

them, they should scarcely profit therewith, since their wives live without rule. But notwithstanding that, I will declare some rules how the married folks should keep themselves in their houses : and how they shall (if they list) avoid strifes and debates between them. For the husbands and the wives having wars together, it is impossible there should be peace in the common wealth. And though this present writing hath not profited me, unlucky and unfortunate man, yet it may profit others which have good wives. For oft times the medicine which profiteth not for the tender eyes sufficeth to heal the hard heels.

'I know well, Faustine, that for what I have said and for that I will say unto thee, thou and others such like shall greatly envy me. Ye will mark the words that I speak, more than the intention that I mean : but I protest before the Gods, that in this case my end is for no other intent, but to advertise the good whereof there are a great many : and to punish the evil, which are many more. And though perchance neither the one nor the other will believe that my intention in speaking these things was good : yet therefore I will not cease to know the good from the evil, and to choose the evil from the good. For in my fantasy the good wife is as the pheasant whose feathers we little esteem and regard much the body, but the evil woman is as the marten whose skin we greatly esteem and utterly despise the flesh. I will therefore declare the rules whereby the husbands may live in peace with their own proper wives.

¶ *The rules are these.*

¶ 'The first, the husband must needs have patience and suffer his wife when she is displeased : for in Lybia there is no serpent so spiteful as an evil woman when she is vexed.

¶ 'The second, the husband ought to provide for his wife (according to his ability) all that is necessary for her, as well for her person as for her house : for oft times it chanceth, that women seeking things necessary, find things superfluous, and not very honest.

¶ 'The third, the husband ought to provide that his wife do keep good company, for women oft times are more troubled with the words that their evil neighbours speak against them, than for any occasion that their husbands give them.

¶ 'The fourth, that the husband ought to use a mean that his wife be not too much a subject, nor that she stray too much abroad: for the woman that gaddeth too much in the theatres both loseth her good name and spendeth his goods.

¶ 'The fifth, the husband ought to take heed that he striveth not so with his wife that she be brought past shame: for the woman that towards her husband is shameless, hath no respect what dishonesty she committeth.

¶ 'The sixth, the husband ought to let his wife understand that he doth trust her: for the woman is of such condition that that which a wise man would not she should do she will do soonest, and that wherein she should take pains, she will do nothing.

¶ 'The seventh, the husband ought to be circumspect that he do not wholly trust his wife with the goods and treasures of the house nor yet utterly distrust her: for if the wife have the charge of the goods of the house, truly she will augment little, and if the husband do suspect her, she will steal much.

¶ 'The eighth, the husband ought to look upon his wife merrily, and at other times again sadly: for women are of such condition that when their husbands show them a merry countenance, they love them, and when they show themselves demure, they fear them.

¶ 'The ninth, the husband ought (if he be wise) in this to take good advisement, that his wife quarrel not with his neighbours, for we have oft times seen in Rome, that for the quarrel of his wife against his neighbour, the husband hath lost his life, she hath lost her goods, and a slander has risen through the common wealth.

¶ 'The tenth, the husband ought to be so patient, that if he saw his wife commit any fault in no wise he should correct her openly but in secret : for the husband that correcteth his wife before witness, doth as he which spitteth into the element, and the spittle falleth again into his eyes.

¶ 'The eleventh, the husband ought to have much temperance lest he lay hands on his wife to punish her, for truly the wife that with sharp words doth not amend, with all the chastisements of the world will never be good.

¶ 'The twelfth, if the husband will live in quiet with his wife, he ought to praise her before his neighbours and strangers : for amongst all other things women have this property, that of all they would be praised and none corrected.

¶ 'The thirteenth, the husband ought to beware to praise any other than his own wife, she being present : for women are of this condition, that the same day the husband commendeth any other woman, the same day his wife will cast him out of her heart, thinking that he loveth another and despiseth her.

¶ 'The fourteenth, the husband ought to

F

make his wife believe she is fair, though indeed she be foul : for there is between them no greater strife than to think that her husband forsaketh her for being foul.

¶ 'The fifteenth, the husband ought to put his wife in remembrance of the infamy, that they speak of them that be evil in the city : for women are glorious, and because they would be loth that men should talk such things by them as they talk of others, peradventure they will refrain from those vices that others commit.

¶ 'The sixteenth, the husband ought to take heed that his wife accept no new friends : for through accepting of new friends there grows commonly between them great dissension.

¶ 'The seventeenth, he ought to take heed that his wife believe that he loveth not them whom she hateth : for women are of such a condition that if the husbands loveth all them that they hate, immediately they will hate all those which they love.

¶ 'The eighteenth, the husband ought sometimes in matters which are not prejudicial unto him, confess himself to be overcome : for women desire rather to be counted the best in reasoning (though it be of no value) than to have otherwise a greater jewel given them.

¶ 'In this sort, Faustine, I will say no more

to thee, but wish that thou shouldst see what I see, and feel what I feel : and above all, that my dissimulation should suffice to amend the life.'

The Emperor answereth more particularly concerning the Key of his Study.
[Chap. xvij.]

¶ 'Now, Faustine, since I have the old venom from my heart expelled, I will answer to thy present demand: for unto demands and answers that passeth between the sages, the tongue ought never to speak word, but that first he ask the heart licence. And it is a general rule among the physicians that the medicines do not profit the sick, unless they first take away the oppilations of the stomach. I mean by this, that no man can speak to his friend (as he ought) unless before he showeth what things grieveth him : for it is better to repair the roofs of the houses that be old, than to go about to build them new.

¶ 'Thou requirest, Faustine, that I give thee the key of my study and thou dost threaten me that if I give it not unto thee that thou shalt forthwith be delivered. I marvel not at that thou sayest, neither I am abashed of that thou demandest, nor yet of that thou wouldst do : for you women are very extreme in your desires, very suspicious

in your demands, very obstinate in your wills,
and as unpatient in your sufferings.

‘ I say not without a cause that women
are extreme in their desires : for there are
things whereof women are so desirous, that
it is wonder though never living creature
saw them nor heard speak of them.

‘ I have not said without a cause that
women are suspicious in their demands, for
the Roman women are of such a condition,
that as soon as a woman desireth anything
she forthwith commandeth the tongue to ask
it, the feet to seek it, the eyes to see it, the
hands to feel it, and likewise the heart to
love it.

‘ I say not without a cause that women
are obstinate in their wills : for if a Roman
woman beareth any malice to any man, she
will not forbear to accuse him for any slander,
nor fail to pursue him for any poverty, nor
fear to kill him for any Justice.

‘ I say not without a cause that women are
unpatient to suffer : for many are of such
condition (I say not all) that if a man give
not speedily that which they desire, they
change their colour, their eyes look red, their
tongues run quick, their voices are sharp,
they fret with themselves, they trouble their
neighbours abroad, and are so out of order
that no man dare speak unto them within.

‘ You have this good trade among ye

women that under colour of being with child, you will that your husbands grant ye all your desires. When the sacred Senate, in the time of the valiant Camillus, made a law in favour of the Roman matrons with child, the women at that time longed not so much as they do at this present : but I cannot tell what this presently meaneth, that all ye are anointed with that that is good, and that ye are all desirous of that that is evil. I will tell thee (Faustine) the occasion why this law was made in Rome, and thereby thou shalt see if thou deserveth to enjoy the privilege thereof or no. For the laws are but as yokes under the which the evil doth labour, and they are wings wherewith the good doth fly.

' The case thereof was such that Camillus the valiant captain went forth to the wars, he made a solemn vow to the Mother Berecinthia, that if the gods gave him the victory he would offer unto her an image of silver : and after Camillus won the victory, and that he would have accomplished his vow to the Mother Berecinthia, neither he had any riches nor Rome had any silver. For at that time Rome was rich of virtues, and poor of money. And know thou, Faustine, that our ancient fathers were devout towards the gods, and curious in repairing the temples, the which they

esteemed to be great devotions: and they
were in such sort observed of their vows,
that neither for sloth, nor poverty, they would
omit their promises towards their gods.
And in these things they were so precise,
that they granted to no man any triumph,
unless he did swear that unto the gods he
had made a vow, and afterwards also proved
how he performed it.

¶ 'At that time flourished in Rome many
virtuous Romans, and many Greek Philosophers, many hardy Captains, and many
sumptuous buildings, and, above all things,
Rome was unpeopled of malices, and adorned
with virtuous ladies. The Historiographers
made (and not without cause) great account
of these virtuous matrons : for the common
wealth hath as much need of virtuous
Women as the wars have valiant Captains.
They, being therefore (as they were) so
virtuous and noble matrons (without the
motion of any woman) determined all to go
into the high Capitol, and there to offer all
their jewels and treasures that they had,
their chains, their rings, their garments, their
bracelets, their girdles, their buttons, and
hangers of gold, of silver, and precious stones
of all sorts, with all their tablets. The
Annals of this time say, that after the Roman
women had laid so great a multitude of
riches at the feet of the sacred senate, in the

name of them all, one of them spake whose
name was called Lucina, and said in this
sort :

' " Fathers conscript, esteem not much
these our jewels, which we give you to make
the image of the mother Berecinthia : but
esteem much this, that we willingly put in
jeopardy our husbands, and children, to win
you the victory. And in this case you accept
our poor service, have no respect to the little
which we do offer, but to the great which
(if we were able) we would give."

' Truly the Romans, though the treasure
which their wives offered was great, yet notwithstanding, they did more esteem the
goodwill wherewith they gave it than they
did the gifts themselves. For there was so
much indeed that sufficeth both to make the
image of the Goddess Berecinthia and also
for a long time to maintain the wars. Therefore, from that day that those matrons presented their jewels in the high Capitol, the
Senate forthwith in remembrance of the
gentleness, granted them these five things as
a privilege. For at that time Rome never
received service, or benefit of any person,
but she rewarded it with double payment.

¶ ' The first thing that the Senate granted
the Roman women was : that in the day of
their burial, the orators might openly make
orations in the praise of their lives : for in

old time men used neither to exalt them when they were dead, nor yet to accompany them to their graves.

¶ 'The second thing that was granted them was, that they might sit in the temples : for in the old time, when the Romans did offer sacrifices to their Gods, the aged did always sit, the priests kneel, the married men did lean, but the women, though they were of noble and high lineage, could neither be suffered to talk, sit, nor to lean.

¶ 'The third thing that the Senate granted the women of Rome was that every one of them might have two rich gowns, and that they should not ask the Senate leave to wear them : for in the old time, if any women were apparelled, or did buy any new gown without asking licence of the Senate, she should immediately remove her gown, and because her husband condescend unto the same, he was banished the common wealth.

¶ 'The fourth thing which they granted them was that they should drink wine when they were sick, for there was in Rome a custom inviolable, that though their life was in hazard, they durst not drink wine but water. For when Rome was well corrected, a woman that drank wine was as much slandered among the people as if she had committed adultery towards her husband.

¶ 'The fifth thing granted by the Senate

unto the women was, that a man might not deny a Roman, being with child, any honest and lawful thing that she demanded. I cannot tell why the ancients of Rome esteemed more women with child than others that had no children.

¶ 'All these things were justly granted to the matrons and noble Roman Ladies. And I can tell thee, Faustine, that they were of the Senate most willingly granted. For it is reason that women which in virtues do excel, should with all means be honoured. I will tell thee, Faustine, the especial cause that moved the Romans to grant unto you matrons this last privilege. That is to wit, that a man cannot deny them anything being with child. Thou oughtest to know that the others (as well Greeks as Latins) did never give laws nor institutions unto their people without great occasions: for the great multitude of laws are commonly evil kept, and on the other part are cause of sundry troubles. We cannot deny but that the ancients did well avoid the great number of institutions : for it is better for a man to live as reason commandeth him, than as the law constraineth him.

'The case therefore was, that in the year of the foundation of Rome 364, Fulvius Torquatus then being Consul, in the war against the Volces, the knights of Mauritania, brought to Rome a huge monster with one eye, called Monoculus : which he had found in the deserts of Egypt. At that time the wife of Torquatus called Macrina, should have been delivered of a child : for the Consul did leave her great. This Macrina amongst all was so honest that they spent as much time in Rome to praise her for her virtues, as they did set forth her husband for his victories. They read in the Annals of that time, that the first time that this Consul Torquatus went into Asia, he was eleven years out of his country, and it is found for a truth that in all the time that Torquatus was absent, his wife was never seen look out at the window, which was not a thing small esteemed : for though it was a custom in Rome to keep the door shut, it was lawful notwithstanding to speak to women at the windows. Though men at that time were not so bold, and the women were so honest : yet Macrina, wife to Torquatus, lived so close and solitary to herself, that in all these eleven years there was never man that saw her go through Rome, nor that ever saw her door open, neither that she consented at any time (from the time that she was eight years of age) that any man should enter into her house : and, moreover, there was never man saw her face wholly uncovered. This Roman Lady did this, to leave of her a memory : and to give example of her virtue. She had also three children, whereof the eldest was but five years old : and so, when they were eight years of age, immediately she sent them out of her house towards their parents, lest under the colour to visit the children others should come to visit her.

' O Faustine, how many have I heard that have lamented this excellent Roman, and what will they think that shall follow her life. Who could presently restrain a Roman woman from going to the window eleven years, since things nowadays are so dissolute, that they do not only desire to see them, but also run in the streets to babble of them? Who should cause nowadays a Roman woman, that in the eleven years she should not open her doors, since it is so, that when the husband commanded her to shut one door, she will make the whole house to ring of her voice ? He that would now command his wife to tarry at home and let her of her vagaries into the town, shall perceive that there is no Basilisk nor Viper that carrieth such poison in her tail, as she will spit with her tongue. Who could make a Roman woman to be eleven years continually without showing her face to any man : since it is so that they spend the most part of their time in looking in the glass, setting their ruffs, brushing their clothes, and painting their faces ? Who would cause a Roman woman to keep herself eleven years from being visited of her neighbours, and friends, since it is true that now women think them greatest enemies, which visit them most seldom ?

' Returning therefore to the monster, as they led this monster before the door of Torquatus house, she being great with child, and her husband in the war : by chance a maid of his told her how that this monster passed by, wherefore so great a desire took her to see the monster that for to keep that she had begun, suddenly for this desire she died. Truly I tell thee, Faustine, that this monster had passed many times by the street where she dwelt, and she would never notwithstanding go to the window : and much less go out of her door to see it.

' The death of this Roman of many was lamented, for it was a long time that Rome had never heard of so honest and virtuous a Roman, wherefore at the petition of all the' Roman people, and by the commandment of all the sacred Senate, they set on her tomb these verses :

¶ The worthy *Macrine* resteth here in grave
   Whom wise *Torquatus* lodged in *Juno's* bed ;
Who reckoned not a happy life to have,
   So that for aye her honest fame was spread.

¶ 'Behold therefore, Faustine, in my opinion, the law was not made to remedy the death of this noble Roman, since she was already dead : but to the end that you Princesses should take example of her life, and that through all Rome there should be a memory of her death. It is reason, since the law was ordained for those women which are honest, that it should be observed in none but upon those which are virtuous : let the women with child mark the words of the law which command them to ask things honest. Wherefore I let ye know, Faustine, that in the seventh table of our laws are written these words : " We will that where there is corruption of manners, the man shall not be bound to observe their liberties." '

FROM

' The thirde booke of the Diall of Princes,
with the famous booke of Marcus Aurelius,
where he entreateth of the vertues which
princes ought to have, as Justice,
peace, and magnificence.'

Of an Oration which a villain dwelling near to the River of Danuby made before the Senators of Rome concerning the tyrannies and oppressions which their officers used in his country. The Oration is divided into three chapters. [Chap. iij.]

¶ In the tenth year of the reign of the good Emperor Marcus Aurelius there happened in Rome a general pestilence : the which being so outrageous, the good Emperor went into Campaigne, which at that time was very healthful, and without diseases, though it was very dry, and wanted much of that which was necessary : yet notwithstanding, the good Emperor was there with all the principal Senators of Rome. For in time of pestilence men do not seek where they shall rejoice their persons, but where they may save their lives. Marcus Aurelius being there in Campaignia was sore vexed with the fever, and as his condition was always to be amongst sages, so at that time his sickness required to be visited of physicians. The resort that he had in his palace was very

G

great, as well of philosophers for to teach, as
of physicians for to dispute. For this Prince
ordained his life in such sort that in his
absence things touching the war were well
provided : and in his presence was nothing
but matters of knowledge argued.

It chanced one day as Marcus Aurelius was
environed with Senators, Philosophers, Physicians and other sage men, a question was
moved among them how greatly Rome was
changed, not only in buildings, which almost
were utterly decayed, but also in manners,
which were wholly corrupted : the cause of
all this evil grew for that Rome was full of
flatterers, and destitute of those which durst
say the truth. These and such other like
words heard, the Emperor took up his hand
and blessed him, and declared unto them a
notable example, saying :

' In the first year that I was Consul there
came a poor villain from the river of Danuby
to ask justice of the Senate against a Censor
which did sore oppress the people and indeed
he did so well propound his complaint, and
declare the folly and injuries which the judges
did in his country, that I doubt whether
Marcus Cicero could utter it better with his
tongue, or the renowned Homer have written
it more eloquently with his pen. This villain
had a small face, great lips, hollow eyes, his
colour burnt, curled hair, bare headed, his

shoes of Porpyge [1] skin, his coat of goatskin, his girdle of bulrushes, a long beard and thick, his eyebrows covered his eyes, the stomach and the neck covered with skins, haired as a bear, and a club in his hand. Without doubt when I saw him enter into the Senate I imagined it had been a beast in the form of a man, and after I heard that which he said I judged him to be a God (if there are gods) amongst men. For if it was a fearful thing to behold his person, it was no less monstrous to hear his words.

' At that time there was great press at the door of the Senate, of many and divers persons, for to solicit the affairs of their provinces : yet notwithstanding this villain spake before the others for two causes. The one, for that men were desirous to hear what so monstrous a man would say : the other, because the Senators had this custom, that the complaints of the poor should be heard before the requests of the rich. Wherefore this villain afterwards in the middle of the Senate began to tell his tale, and the cause of his coming thither : in the which he showed himself no less bold in words than he was in his attire strange, and said unto them in this sort :

' " O fathers conscript, and happy people,

[1] Sp. *puerco espine*, Fr. *porc espic*, porcupine : but porpoise-hide seems the more likely material.

I, Mileno, a ploughman, dwelling near unto the River of Danuby, do salute you worthy Senators of Rome which are convented here in this Senate, and I beseech the immortal gods my tongue this day so to govern, that I may say that which is convenient for my country, and that they help you others to govern well the common wealth. For without the help of God, we can neither learn the good, nor avoid the evil. The fatal destinies permitting it, and our wrathful gods forsaking us, our mishap was such, and to ye others fortune showed herself so favourable, that the proud captains of Rome by force of arms took our country of Germany. And I say not without a cause that at that time the gods were displeased with us : for if we Germans had appeased our gods, ye Romans might well have excused yourselves for overcoming of us. Great is your glory, O Romans, for the victories ye have had, and triumphs which of many realms ye have conquered : but notwithstanding greater shall your infamy be in the world to come for the cruelties which you have committed. For I let you know, if you do not know it, that when the wicked went before the triumphing chariots saying, 'Live, live, invincible Rome!' on the other side the poor captives went saying in their hearts, ' Justice ! Justice ! '

' " My predecessors, inhabited by the river

of Danuby, for when the dry earth annoyed them, they came to re-create themselves in the fresh water: and if perchance the unconstant water did annoy them, then they would return again to the mainland. And as the appetites and conditions of men are variable, so there is a time to fly from the land, to refresh ourselves by the water : and time also when we are annoyed with the water to return again to the land.

' " But how shall I speak, Romans, that which I would speak ? Your covetousness of taking other men's goods has been so extreme, and your pride of commanding strange countries hath been so disordinate, that neither the sea can suffice you in the deepness thereof, neither the land assure us in the fields of the same. O, how great comfort it is for the troubled men, to think and be assured that there are just gods, the which will do justice on the unjust. For if the oppressed men thought themselves not assured that the gods would wreak their injury of their enemies, they with their own hands would destroy themselves.

' " The end where I speak this is, for so much as I hope in the just gods, that as you others without reason have cast us out of our houses, so by reason shall others come after us, and cast you others out of Italy and Rome both. There in my country of Ger-

many, we take it for a rule infallible, that he
which by force taketh the goods of another
by reason ought to lose his own proper right.
And I hope in the gods that that which we
have for a proverb in Germany, you shall
have for experience here in Rome. By the
gross words I speak, and by the strange
apparel which I wear, you may well imagine
that I am some rude villain or barbarous
born : but yet, notwithstanding, I want not
reason to know who is just and righteous in
holding his own : and who is a tyrant in
possession of others. For the rude men of
my profession, though in good style they
cannot declare that which they would utter :
yet notwithstanding, we are not ignorant of
that which ought to be allowed for good,
nor which ought to be condemned for
evil.

' " I would say therefore in this case, that
that which the evil with all their tyranny
have gathered in many days, the gods shall
take from them in one hour : and contrarywise, all that which the good shall lose in
many years, the gods shall restore to them
in one minute. For speaking the truth, the
evil to prosper in riches, is not for that the
gods will it, but that they do suffer it, and
though at this hour we complain dissembling,
we suffer much, but the time shall come
that will pay for all. Believe me in one

thing, O Romans, and doubt not therein : that of the unlawful gain of the fathers, followeth after the just undoing of their children.

‘ “ Many oftentimes do marvel in my country, what the cause is that the gods do not take from the wicked that which they win, immediately as soon as they win it : and as I think the reason hereof is, for that dissembling with them, by little and little they gather together divers things, and afterwards when they think least thereon, it is taken from them all at once. For the just judgment of the gods is, that since without reason they have done evil to others : others by reason should come in like manner which do evil unto them.

‘ “ It is impossible that the valiant and sage man, who in his deeds presumeth to be wise, should take any taste in another man’s good : for if he did, he would never content himself with anything, since he hath not a conscience in that which is evil gotten. I know not, Romans, whether you understand me, but because you shall understand me better, I say, that I marvel, and I should rather wonder, how the man keeping another man’s goods can sleep or rest one hour, since he knoweth he hath done injury to the gods, slandered his neighbours, pleased his enemies, lost his friends, and endamaged those that he robbed, and worst of all that he hath put his person in peril. And I say, that he hath put his person in peril : for the day that any man determineth to take my goods, he will also the same day (if he can) take my life.

' " It is an odious thing to the gods, and very slanderous among men, that men should have so much (through their fleshly desires) virtue bound, and the rain of their evil works so much at liberty, that another man's misery seemeth to him riches, and that his own riches seemeth to himself poverty. I care not whether he be Greek, barbarous, Roman, present or absent, I say and affirm, that he is and shall be cursed of the gods and hated of men, which without considera-tion will change his good name into shame, justice into wrong, right into tyranny, truth into lies, the certain for the doubtful, hating his own proper, and sighing for that of other men. He that hath his chief intention to gather goods for his children, and seeketh not a good name among the renowned, it is just that such one do not only lose the goods which he hath gathered, but also that without good name he remain shameful among the wicked.

' " Since you other Romans naturally are proud, and pride doth blind you, you think yourselves happy, that for having so much as ye have more than others, that therefore you should be more honoured than all, the which truly is not so. For if presently you will not open your eyes and confess your own errors, you shall see, that whereas you avaunt yourselves to be lords of strange provinces, you shall find yourselves made slaves with your own proper goods. Gather as much as you will, let them do all you do command them : yet as I think it little availeth to have plebeian's houses with goods, and contrarywise the hearts to be possessed with covetousness. For the riches which are gotten with covetousness, and are kept with avarice, do take away the good name from the possessor, and do nothing avail to maintain his life. It cannot be suffered many days, and much less hid many years, that one man should be counted both for rich among the rich, and for honoured among the honourable : for it is impossible that he which is a great lover of temporal goods, should be a friend of his good name. O if the covetous men were of their own honour as greedy, as they are of the goods of another desirous, I swear unto you by the immortal gods that the little worm or moth of covetousness would not gnaw the rest of their life, nor the canker of infamy should destroy their good name after their death.

' " Hearken, you Romans, hearken what I

will say, and I beseech the gods that you may understand it, for otherwise I should lose my labour, and ye others should take no fruit of my words. I see that all the world hateth pride, and yet there is none that will follow humanity. Every man condemneth adultery, and yet I see no man that liveth chaste. Every man curseth excess, and I see no man live temperately. Every man praiseth patience, and I see no man that will suffer. Every man blameth sloth, and I see no man but those that are idle. Every one blameth avarice, and yet every man robbeth. One thing I say, and not without tears in this Senate, openly I do declare it, which is, that with the tongue every man praiseth virtue : and yet they themselves, with all their limbs, are servants unto vices. Do not think that I say this only for the Romans which be in Illiria : but for the Senators which I see here in the Senate. All you Romans, in your devices about your arms, have this for your word, *Romanorum est debellare superbos, et parcere subjectis.* Truly, you should better have said, *Romanorum est spoliare innocentes et reddere subjectos,* for you Romans are but destroyers of the people that be peaceable, and robbers of the sweat and labours of strangers." '

The villain argueth against the Romans, which without cause or reason conquered their country, and proved manifestly that they through offending of their gods were vanquished of the Romans. [Chap. iv.]

¶ ' " I ask ye Romans what occasion ye have, that are brought up nigh to the river of Tiber, against us that live in peace nigh to the river of Danuby. Peradventure you have seen us friends to your foes, or else we have showed ourselves your enemies ? Peradventure you have heard say, that forsaking our own land we should go conquer foreign realms ? Peradventure ye have been advertised, that we rebelling against our own lords, should become obedient to the cruel barbarous ? Peradventure ye have sent us some ambassador to desire us to be your friends : or else there came some from us to Rome, to defy ye as our enemies ? Peradventure some king died in our realm, which by his testament made ye heirs to our realm : whereby you claim your title, and like to make us your subjects ? Peradventure, by some ancient law or custom ye have found, that the noble and worthy Germany of necessity is subject to the proud people of Rome ? Peradventure we have destroyed your armies, we have wasted your fields, sacked your cities, spoiled your subjects, or

favoured your enemies, so that to revenge
these injuries ye should destroy our land ?
If we had been your neighbours, or you ours,
it had been no marvel though one should
have destroyed the other. For it chanceth
oftentime that through controversy of a
little piece of ground, tedious wars between
people arise.

' " Of a truth none of all these things which
I have named hath chanced between ye
Romans and us Germans. For in Germany
we felt your tyranny, so soon as we heard of
your renown. If ye be grieved with that I
have said, I pray you be not offended with
that I will say, which is, that the name of
Romans, and the cruelty of tyrants, arrived
together in one day upon our people. And
what more to say I know not, Romans, of
the little care the gods do take, and of the
great audacity that men have. For I see
that he which possesseth much doth oppress
him which hath but little : and he that hath
but little, weigheth not him that hath much.
So disordered covetousness striveth with
secret malice, and secret malice giveth place
to open theft and open robbery : no man
resisteth, and thereof cometh, that the covetousness of a malicious man is accomplished,
to the prejudice of a whole state.

' " Hearken, ye Romans, hearken, by the
immortal gods I do conjure you, give ear

to that I will say, which is, consider well what you have done : for the gods' words be in vain, or else men must have an end, the world in time must needs fall, or else the world shall be no world. Fortune must needs make sure the pin of the wheel, or else that shall be seen which never was seen, which is, that which in eight years ye have won, ye shall within eight days lose. For nothing can be more just, since ye by force have made yourselves tyrants, than that the gods by justice should make you slaves : and do not think, ye Romans, though you have subdued Germany, and be lords thereof, that it was by any warly industry : for ye are no more warlike, no more courageous nor more hardy, nor yet more valiant than we Germans : but since through our offences we have provoked the gods to wrath, they for the punishment of our disordinate vices ordained, that ye should be a cruel plague and scourge to our persons. Do not take yourselves to be strong, neither repute us to be so weak, that if the gods at the time had favoured the one part, as much as the other, it might perchance have happened, ye should not have enjoyed the spoil. For to say the truth, you won not the victory through the force of weapons, that you brought from Rome : but through the infinite vices, which ye found in Germany.

' " Therefore, since we were not overcome for being cowards, neither for being weak, nor yet for being fearful, but only for being wicked, and not having the gods favourable unto us, what hope ye Romans to become of you, being as you are vicious, and having the gods angry with you ?   Do not think, Romans, to be the more victorious, for that ye assemble great armies, or that ye abound in treasures, neither for that you have greater gods in your aid, or that ye build greater temples, nor yet for that ye offer such great sacrifices.   For I let you know, if ye do not know it, that no man is in more favour with the gods, than he which is at peace with virtue.   If the triumphs of the conquerors consisteth in nothing else but in subtle wits, politic captains, valiant soldiers, and great armies, without doubt it would little avail to carry all this to the war, since afterwards we see by experience, that men can do no more but give the battles, and the gods themselves must give the victory.

' " If I be not deceived, I think that for our offences we have sufficiently satisfied the gods' wrath.   But truly I believe that the cruelties which you have done unto us, and the unthankfulness which you have showed the gods (though as yet ye have not paid it) yet once ye shall pay it.   And hereafter it may chance that as presently ye count us for

slaves, so in time to come ye shall acknowledge us for lords.

' " Since that, travelling by the way, I
have seen the high mountains, divers provinces, sundry nations, countries so savage,
peoples so barbarous, such and so many miles
as Germany is distant from Rome, I muse
what fond toy came in the Romans' heads
to send to conquer Germany ? If covetousness of treasures caused it, I am sure they
spent more money to conquer it, and at this
present do spend to keep it, than the whole
revenues of Germany amounteth, or may
amount in many years : and perchance they
may lose it before they recover that they
spent to conquer it. And if ye say unto me,
Romans, that Germany is not conquered of
Rome for ever, but that only Rome should
have the glory to be mistress of Germany,
this also I say is vanity and folly. For
little availeth it to have the forts and castles
of the people: when the hearts of the inhabit-
ants are out of them. If ye say that therefore ye conquered Germany, to amplify and
enlarge the limits and bounds of Rome, also
methinketh this as foolish an enterprise. For
it is not the point of wise and valiant men to
enlarge their dominions, and diminish their
honour. If ye say ye sent to conquer us to
the end we should not be barbarous, nor live
like tyrants, but that you would we should

live after your good laws and customs, if it
be so I am well content. But how is it
possible ye should give laws to strangers,
when you break the laws of your own predecessors ? Great shame ought they to
have, which take upon them to correct others
when they have more need to be corrected
themselves : for the blind man ought not
to take upon him to lead the lame.

' " If this be true (as presently it is) what
reason or occasion had proud Rome, to take
and conquer the innocent Germany ? Let
us all go therefore to rob, to kill, to conquer,
to spoil, since we see the world so corrupt,
and so far from the love of God, that every
man (as we may perceive) taketh what he
can, killeth whom he will and that which
worst of all is, that neither those which
govern will remedy so many evils as are
committed, neither those which are offended
dare complain. Ye chief judges at this day
are so hard to be entreated, ye take so little regard unto the poor oppressed: that they think
it more quiet to remain in trouble at home,
than to come and put up their complaints
before you here at Rome. And the cause
hereof is, that there in their country they
have but one which pursueth them : and here
in this Senate they are evil willed of all, and
that is because he which complaineth is poor,
and the other which is complained on is rich.

' " Therefore, since fortune would it and the fatal destinies permit it, that the proud Rome should be mistress of our Germany, it is but reason ye should keep us in justice and maintain us in peace. But you do not so, but rather those which come thither do take from us our goods, and ye that are here do rob us of our good name, saying that since we are a people without law, without reason, and without a king (as unknown barbarous), ye may take us for slaves.

' " In this case ye Romans are greatly deceived, for me thinketh with reason ye cannot call us without reason, since we being such as we are, and as the gods created us, remain in our proper countries, without desiring to seek or invade foreign realms. For with more reason we might say that ye were men without reason, being not contented with the sweet and fertile Italy : but that through shedding of blood you should desire to conquer all the earth.

' " In that ye say we deserve to be slaves, because we have no prince to command us, nor senate to govern us, nor army to defend us, to this I will answer, that since we had no enemies, we needed no armies, and since every man is contented with his lot and fortune, we had no necessity of a proud senate to govern us, and we being as we are all equal, it need not we should

H

consent to have any princes amongst us.
For the office of princes is to suppress tyrants,
and to maintain the people in peace.

' " If ye say further that we have not in
our country a commonwealth, nor policy,
but that we live as the brute beasts in the
mountains, in this also you have also but
small reason. For we in our country did
suffer no liars, neither rebels, nor seditious
persons, nor men that brought us (from strange
countries) any apparel for to be vicious, so
that since in apparel we were honest, and in
meat very temperate, we needed no better
behaviour. For although in our country
there are no merchants of Carthage, oil of
Mauritania, merchants of Tyre, steel of Cantabria, odours of Asia, gold of Spain, silver
of Britain, amber of Sidonia, silk of Dam-
ascus, corn of Sicily, wine of Candy, purple
of Araby : yet for all this we are not brutish,
neither cease to have a commonwealth.
For these and such other like things give
more occasion to stir up many vices, than
for virtuous men to live according to virtue.
Blessed and happy is the commonwealth,
not where great riches aboundeth, but where
virtues are highly commended : nor where
many light and angry men resort, but where
the patient are resident : therefore it followeth : that of the commonwealth of Rome
for being rich, we should have pity : and of

the commonwealth of Germany for being
poor, ye ought to have envy. Would to
God that the contentation we have with our
poverty, ye others had the same with your
riches. For then neither ye had robbed us
of our countries, nor we had not come hither
now to complain in Rome of your tyranny.
I see, Romans, that the one differeth much
from the other. For ye others, though ye
hear our oppressions, yet thereby ye lose
not your pastime : but we others can never
dry the tears of our eyes, nor cease to bewail
our infinite misfortunes." '

*The Villain concludeth his oration against the
judges, which minister not justice, and
declareth how prejudicial such wicked
men are unto the public weal.* [Chap. v.]

¶ ' " Ye would think I have said that I
can say, but certainly it is not so. For
there remaineth many things to speak, which
to hear ye will be astonished, yet be ye
assured, that to speak them I will not be
afraid, since you others in doing them are
not ashamed. For open offence deserveth
not secret correction.
' " I marvel much at ye Romans, what ye
meaned to send (as you did) such ignorant
judges, the which (by the immortal gods I

swear) can neither declare us your laws, and much less they can understand ours. And the cause of this evil is, that ye sent not to us those which be best able to minister justice in Germany, but those which have best friends with you in Rome : presuppose that to those of the Senate ye gave the office of censorship more for importunity than for ability. It is little that I can say here in respect they dare do there. That which ye command them here, I know not : but of that which they do there, I am not ignorant, which is—Your judges take all bribes that are brought unto them openly : and they pool and thieve as much as they can secretly. They grievously punish the offences of the poor, and dissemble with the faults of the rich : they consent to many evils, to have occasion to commit greater thefts : they forget the government of the people to take their pleasure in vice. And being there to mitigate slanders, they are those which are most slanderous : and without goods it availeth no man to ask Justice. And finally, under the colour that they be judges of Rome, they fear not to rob all the land of Germany.

' "What meaneth this, ye Romans, shall your pride never have end in commanding, nor your covetousness in robbing ? Say unto us what ye will in words, but oppress us not so in deeds. If you do it for our children, load them with irons and make them slaves, for ye cannot charge them with more than they are able to carry : but of commandments and tributes ye gave us more than we were either able to carry, or suffer. If you do it for our goods, go thither and take them all. For in our country we do not use as ye Romans do, nor have such conditions as ye have here in Rome. For you desire to live poor because you desire to die rich. If ye say that we will rebel, I marvel what you should mean to think so, since ye have spoiled us, robbed us, and handled us ill. Assure me, ye Romans, that ye will not unpeople us, and I will assure you we will not rebel. If our service do not content thee, strike off our heads as to the evil men. For (to tell ye the truth) the knife shall not be so fearful to our necks, as you tyrants be abhorred in our hearts.

' " Do you know what ye have done, ye Romans ? Ye have caused us of that miserable realm to swear, neither to dwell with our wives, and to slay our own children, rather than to leave them in the hands of so cruel and wicked tyrants as ye be. For we had rather they should die in liberty, than live in bondage. As desperate men we have determined to suffer, and endure the beastly motions of the flesh, during the time we have to live, to the end we will not get our wives with child. For we had rather live chaste twenty or thirty years, than to leave our children perpetual slaves. If it be true that the children must endure, that which the miserable fathers do suffer, it is not only good to slay them, but also it should be better not to agree they should be born. Ye ought not to do this, Romans, for the land taken by force ought the better to be governed, to the intent that the miserable captives seeing justice duly administered, presently should thereby forget the tyranny past, and content themselves with perpetual servitude.

' " And since it is true, that we are come to complain of the oppressions which your officers do here upon the river of Danuby, peradventure ye which are of the Senate will hear us : and though you are now determined to hear us, yet you are slow to remedy us : so that before ye began to reform an evil custom the whole common wealth is already undone. I will tell you of some things thereof, so that you may know them, and then to reform them.

' " If there come a right poor man to demand justice, having no money to give, nor wine to present, nor oil to promise, nor friends to help him, nor revenue to succour him, and maintain him in expenses : after he hath complained they satisfy him with words, saying unto him that speedily he shall have justice. What will ye I should say, but that in the meantime they make him spend the little he hath, and give him nothing though he demand much, they give him vain hope, and they make him waste the best of his life, every one of them doth promise him favour, and afterwards they all lay hands upon him to oppress him. The most of them say his right is good, and afterwards they give sentence against him : so that the miserable person which came to complain of one, returneth home complaining of all, cursing his cruel destinies, and crying out to the just and merciful gods for revengement.

' " It chanceth, also, that oft times there cometh to complain here in the Senate some flattering man more for malice than by reason of right, or justice : and ye Senators crediting his double words, and his feigned tears, immediately ordain a Censor to go and give audience on their complaints. Who being gone and returned, ye seek more to remedy and give ear to the complaints of the judge, than to the slanders which were among the people. I will declare unto you my life, O ye Romans, and thereby ye shall see how they pass their life in my country.

' " I live by gathering acorns in the winter, and reaping corn in the summer. Sometimes

I fish, as well of necessity as of pleasure, so that I pass almost all my life alone in the fields, or in the mountains. And if you wote not why, hear me, and I will show you. I see such tyranny in your judges, and such robberies as they commit among the poor people, and there are such dissensions in the realm, such injuries committed therein, the poor commonwealth is so spoiled, there are so few that have desire to do good, and also there are so few that hope for remedy in the Senate : that I am determined (as most unhappy) to banish myself out of mine own house, and to separate myself from my sweet company, and to the end my eyes should not behold so miserable a change. For I had rather wander solitary in the fields, than to see my neighbours hourly lament in the streets. For there the cruel beasts do not offend me, unless I do assault them : but the cursed men, though I do serve them, yet daily they vex me.

‘ “ Without doubt it is a marvellous pain to suffer an overthrow of fortune : but it is a greater torment when one feeleth it without remedy. And yet without comparison my greatest grief is, when my loss may be remedied, and that he which may, will not : and he that will, cannot, by any means remedy it. O cruel Romans, ye feel nothing that we feel, in especially I which speak it, ye shall see how I feel it, since only to reduce it to memory my eyes do dazzle, my tongue wax weary, my joints do shiver, my heart doth tremble, my entrails do break, and my flesh consumeth, what a woeful thing is it in my country to see it with my eyes, to hear it with my ears and to feel it with mine own hands ?

' " Truly, the griefs which the woeful Germany suffereth are such and so many that I believe yet the merciful gods will have compassion upon us. I will not desire ye to think slander of my words : but only I do beseech ye you will understand well what I say. For you imagining (as you do presume to be discreet) shall see right well that the troubles which came to us from men, and among men with men, and by the hands of men, it is a small matter that we as men do feel them speaking. For according to the truth, and also with liberty, if I should declare every other just advertisement which came from the Senate, and all the tyranny which your judges commit in the miserable realm, one of these two things must ensue, either the punishment of me, or the deprivation of your officers if I say true.

' " One thing only comforteth me, whereof I with other unfortunate people have had experience, in that I think myself happy, to know that the just plagues proceed not from the just gods, but through the just deserts of wicked men : and that our secret fault doth waken those, to the end that they of us may execute open justice. Of one thing only I am sore troubled, because the gods cannot be contented, but for a small fault they punish a good man much : and for many faults they punish evil men nothing at all, so that the gods do bear with the one, and forgive nothing unto the other. O secret judgments of God, that as I am bound to praise your works, so likewise if I had licence to condemn them, I durst say, that ye cause us to suffer grievous pains for that ye punish and persecute us by the hands of such judges, the which (if justice took place in the world), when they chastise us with their hands, they do not deserve to have their heads on their shoulders.

' " The cause why now again I do exclaim on the immortal gods is to see, that in these fifteen days I have been at Rome, I have seen such deeds done in your Senate, that if the least of them had been done at Danuby, the gallows and gibbets had been hanged thicker of thieves than the vineyard is with grapes. I am determined to see your doings, to speak of your dishonesty in apparel, your little temperance in eating and your disorder in affairs, and your pleasures in living : and on the other side, I see that when your provision

arriveth in our country, we carry into the
temples and offer it to the gods, we put it on
their heads : so that the one meeting with
the other, we accomplish that which is commanded, and accurse those that commanded.
And since therefore my heart hath now seen
that which it desireth, my mind is at rest,
in spitting out the poison which in it abideth.
If I have in anything here offended with my
tongue, I am ready to make recompense
with my head. For in good faith I had
rather win honour, in offering myself to
death, than ye should have it, in taking
from me my life."

'And here the villain ended his talk.'

Immediately after Marcus Aurelius said to
those which were about him :

'How think ye my friends what kernel of
a nut, what gold of the mine, what corn of
straw, what rose of briars, what marrow of
bones, and how noble and valiant a man hath
he showed himself? What reasons so high,
what words so well couched, what truth so
true, what sentences so well pronounced, and
also what open malice hath he discovered ?
By the faith of a good man I swear, as I may
be delivered from this fever which I have :
I saw this villain standing boldly a whole
hour on his feet, and all we, beholding the
earth as amazed, could not answer him one
word. For indeed this villain confused us

with his purpose, and astonished us to see the little regard he had of his life.

' The Senate afterwards being all agreed, the next day following, we provided new judges for the river of Danuby, and commanded the villain to deliver us by writing, all that he had said by mouth, to the end it might be registered in the book of good saying of strangers, which were in the Senate. And further it was agreed, that the said villain (for the wise words he spake) should be chosen Senator, and of the free men of Rome he should be one, and that forever he should be sustained with the common treasure. For our mother Rome hath always been praised and esteemed, not only to acquite the services which hath been done unto her, but also the good words which were spoken in the Senate.'

II

The Author reciteth the commodities which come of peace declaring how divers princes upon light occasions can make cruel wars.
[Chap. xiij.]

¶ Dimo, an ancient King of Ponto, said unto a philosopher which was with him: ' Tell me, philosopher, I have health, I have honour and I have riches, is there anything

more to be desired amongst men, or to be
given of the gods in this life ? '

The philosopher answered him : ' I see
that I never saw, and I hear that I never
heard. For health, riches, and honour the
gods seldom times do thrust in one person.
His time is so short that possess them, that
they have more reason to pray that they
might be quit of them, than for to be proud
for that they possess them. And I tell thee
further, King Dimo, it little profiteth that
the gods have given thee all these things if
thou dost not content thyself therewith,
the which I think they have not given thee,
nor never will give thee. For the gods are
so just in dividing their gifts, that to them
to whom they give contentation, they take
from them riches : and those whom they
give riches, they take their contentation.'
Plutarch in the first of his politics putteth
this example, and he declareth not the name
of this philosopher.

¶ O how great a benefit is that, which the
gods give to princes and great lords, in
giving them their health, in giving them
honour and in giving them riches : but if
besides those he giveth them not contentation, I say that in giving them the goods, he
giveth them travail and danger. For if the
travail of the poor be greater than the travail
of the rich : without comparison the dis-

contentation of the rich is greater than the discontentation of the poor. Men little regarding their health become sick, little esteeming their riches become poor, and because they know not what honour is they become dishonoured. I mean that the rash princes, until such time as they have been well beaten in the wars, will always little regard peace.

The day that you princes proclaim war against your enemies, you set at liberty all vices to your subjects : yet you say your meaning is not they should be evil. I say it is true : yet all this joined together, ye give them occasion that they be not good. Let us know what thing war is, and then we shall see whether it be good or evil to follow it. In wars, they do nought else but kill men, rob the temples, spoil the people, destroy the innocents, give liberty to thieves, separate friends, and raise strife : all the which things cannot be done without great hurt of justice, and scrupulosity of conscience. The seditious man himself cannot deny us, that if two princes take upon them wars between them, and that both of them seem to have right, yet the one of them only hath reason. So that the prince which shall fight against justice, or defend the unjust cause, shall not escape out of that war justified : not issuing out justified, he shall remain condemned : and the condemnation shall be that all the losses, murders, burnings, hangings, and robberies which were done in the one or other common wealth, shall remain upon the account of him which took upon him the unjust war. Although he doth not find another prince that will demand an account of him here in this life yet he shall have a just judge that will, in another place, lay it to his charge.

The prince which is virtuous, and presumeth to be a Christian, before he begin the war, ought to consider what loss or profit will ensue thereof. Wherein if the end be not prosperous, he loseth his goods and honour : and if he perchance attain to that he desired, peradventure his desire was to the damage of the common wealth, and then he ought not to desire it. For the desire of one should not hurt the profit of all. When God our Lord did create princes for princes, and people accepted them for their lords, it is to believe that the gods never commanded such things, nor the men would have ever accepted such, if they had thought that princes would not have done that they were bound, but rather that whereunto they were inclined. For if men follow that whereunto their sensuality inclineth them, they do always err. Therefore, if they suffer themselves to be governed by reason, they are always sure. And besides that, princes should not take upon them wars, for the burdening of their conscience, the misspending of their goods, and the loss of their honour : they ought also to remember the duties that they owe to the commonwealth, the which they are bound to keep in peace and justice. For we others need not governors to search us enemies, but princes which may defend us from the wicked.

The divine Plato in his fourth book *de legibus* sayeth that one demanded him why he did exalt the Lydians so much, and so much dispraise the Lacedemonians. Plato answered : ' If I commend the Lydians, it is for that they never were occupied but in tilling the field, and if I do reprove here the Lacedemonians, it is because they never knew anything else but to conquer realms. And therefore I say that more happy is that realm where men have their hands with labouring full of blisters, than where their arms in fighting are wounded with swords.'

These words which Plato spake are very true, and would to God that in the gates and hearts of princes they were written. Plinius in an epistle sayeth, that it was a proverb much used amongst the Greeks, that he was king which never saw king. The like may we say, that he only may enjoy peace, which never knew what war meant.

For simple and innocent though a man be, there is none but will judge him more happy, which occupieth his handkerchief to dry the sweat of his brows : than he that breaketh it to wipe the blood of his head. The princes and great lords which are lovers of war, ought to consider that they do not only hurt in general all men, but also specially the good : and the reason is that although they of their own will do abstain from battle, do not spoil, do not rebel, nor slay : yet it is necessary for them to endure the injuries, and to suffer their own loss and damages. For none are meet for the war, but those which little esteem their life, and much less their consciences. If the war were only with the evil against the evil, and to the hurt and hindrance of the evil, little should they feel which presume to be good. But I am sorry the good are persecuted, the good are robbed and the good are slain : for if it were otherwise (as I have said) the evil against the evil, we would take little thought both for the vanquishing of the one, and much less for the destruction of the other.

I ask now what fame, what honour, what glory, what victory, or what riches in that war can be won, wherein so many good, virtuous, and wise men are lost ? There is such penury of the good in the world, and such need of them in the commonwealth, that if it were in our power, we with our tears ought to pluck them out of their graves and give them life, and not lead them into the wars, as to a shambles to be put to death. Pliny in one epistle and Seneca in another say, that when they desired a Roman captain that with his army he should enter into a great danger, whereof great honour should ensue unto him and little profit to the commonwealth, he answered : 'For nothing would I enter into that danger if it were not to give life to a Roman citizen. For I desire rather to go environed with the good in Rome, than to go laden with treasures into my country.' Comparing prince to prince, and law to law, and the Christian with the pagan : without comparison the soul of a Christian ought more to be esteemed than the life of a Roman. For the good Roman observeth it as a law to die in the war : but the good Christian hath the precept, to live in peace.

Suetonius Tranquillus in the second book of Cæsars sayeth, that among all the Roman princes there was no prince so well beloved, nor yet in the wars so fortunate as Augustus was. And the reason hereof is because that prince never began any war, unless by great occasion he was thereunto provoked. O of how many princes (not Ethnicks but Christians) we have heard and read, all contrary to this, which is, that they were of such large conscience, that they never took upon them any war that was just, to whom I swear and promise, that since the war which they in this world began was unjust : the punishment which in another they shall have is most righteous. Xerxes, King of the Perses, being one day at dinner, one brought unto him very fair and savoury figs of the province of Athens : the which being set at the table, he sware by the immortal gods, and by the bones of his predecessors, that he would never eat figs of his country but of Athens, which were the best of all Greece. And that which by word of mouth King Xerxes swear, by valiant deeds with force and shield he accomplished and went forthwith to conquer Greece, for no other cause but for to fill himself with the figs of that country, so that he began that war not only as a light prince, but also as a vicious man.

Titus Livius sayeth that when the Frenchmen did taste of the wine of Italy, immediately they put themselves in arms and went to conquer the country, without having any other occasion to make war against them : so that the Frenchmen for the licorousness of the pleasant wines, lost the dear blood of their own hearts.

King Antigonus dreamed one night that he saw King Mithridates with a scythe in his hand, who like a mower did cut all Italy. And there fell such fear to Antigonus, that he determined to kill King Mithridates : so that this wicked prince for crediting a light dream, set all the world in an uproar.

¶ The Lombards being in Pannonia, heard say that there was in Italy sweet fruits, savoury flesh, odoriferous wines, fair women, good fish, little cold, and temperate heat : the which news moved them not only to desire them, but also they took weapons to conquer Italy : so that the Lombards came not into Italy to revenge them of their enemies, but to be there more vicious and riotous.

The Romans and the Carthagians were friends of long time, but after they knew there was in Spain great mines of gold and silver, immediately arose between them exceeding cruel wars, so that those two puissant realms, for to take each from the other their goods, destroyed their own proper dominions. The authors of the above said were Plutarchus, Paulus Diaconus, Berosus, and Titus Livius.

O secret judgments of God which suffereth such things. O merciful goodness of thee, my Lord, that permitteth such things, that through the dream of one prince in his chamber, another for to rob the treasures of Spain, another to fly the cold of Hungary, another to drink the wines of Italy, another to eat the figs of Greece, should put all the country to fire and blood. Let not my pen be cruel against all princes which have unjust wars. For, as Traian said, ' Just war is more worth than feigned peace.' I commend, approve, and exalt princes which are careful and stout to keep and defend that which their predecessors left them. For admit that for dispossessing them, hereof cometh all the breach with other princes. Look how much his enemy offendeth his conscience for taking it : so much offendeth he his commonwealth for not defending it. The words which the divine Plato spake in the first book of his laws did satisfy me greatly, which were these :

' It is not meet we should be too extreme in commending those which have peace : nor let us be too vehement in reproving those which have war. For it may be now, that if one have war it is to the end to attain peace : and for the contrary, if one have peace it shall be to the end to make war.'

Indeed Plato said very true. For it is more worth to desire short war for long peace, than short peace for long war. The philosopher Chilo being demanded whereby a good or evil governor might be known, he answered, ' There is nothing whereby a good and evil man be better known, than in that for the which they strive. For the tyrannous prince offereth himself to die to take from another : but the virtuous prince travaileth to defend his own. When the Redeemer of this world departed from this world, he said not, ' I give ye my war, or leave ye my war,' but, ' I leave ye my peace, and give you my peace.'

Thereof ensueth that the good Christian is bound to keep the peace, which Christ so much commanded, than to invent war to revenge his proper injury, which God so much hated. If princes did that they ought to do, and in this case would believe me : for no temporal thing they should condescend to shed man's blood, if nothing else, yet at the least the love of Him which on the Cross shed His precious blood for us should from that clean dissuade us. For the good Christians are commanded to bewail their own sins, but they have no license to shed the blood of their enemies. Finally, I desire, exhort, and further admonish all princes, and great Lords, that for His sake that is Prince of Peace, they love peace, procure peace, keep peace, and live in peace. For in peace they shall be rich, and their people happy.

¶ *The Emperor, Marcus Aurelius, writeth to his friend Cornelius, wherein he describeth the discommodities of war and the vanity of triumph.* [Chap. xiv.]

¶ Marcus Emperor wisheth to thee, Cornelius, his faithful friend, health to thy person, and good luck against all evil fortune. Within fifteen days after I came from the war of Asia, whereof I have triumphed here in Rome, remembering that in times past thou wert a companion of my travels, I sent immediately to certify thee of my triumphs. For the noble hearts do more rejoice of their friends' joy than they do of their own proper delights.

If thou wilt take pains to come when I send to call thee, be thou assured that on the one part thou shalt have much pleasure to see the great abundance of riches that I have brought out of Asia, and to behold my receiving into Rome : and on the other, thou canst not keep thyself from weeping to see such a sort of captives (the which entered in before the triumphant chariots), bound and naked, to augment to the conqueror's most glory, and also to them vanquished to be a greater ignominy.

Seldom times we see the sun shine bright all the day long, but first in the summer there hath been a mist or, if it be in the winter,

there hath been a frost.   By this parable I
mean, that one of the miseries of this world
is that we shall see few in this world which
now be prosperous, but before have had fortune, in some cases very malicious.   For we
see by experience some come to be very poor,
and others chance to attain to great riches :
so that through the impoverishing of those,
the other become rich and prosperous.   The
weapon of the one causeth the other to laugh :
so that if the bucket that is empty above
doth not go down, the other which is full
beneath cannot come up.

Speaking   therefore   according   to   sensuality, thou wouldst have been glad that
day to have seen our triumph, with the
abundance of riches, the great number of
captives, the diversity of beasts, the valiantness of the captains, the sharpness of wits
which we brought from Asia and entered
into Rome, whereby thou mightest well
know the dangers that we escaped in the
war.   Wherefore, speaking the truth, the
matter between us and our enemies was so
debated, that those of us that escaped death
had their bodies sore wounded, and their
veins also almost without blood.   I let thee
know, my Cornelius, that the Parthes are
warlike men, and in dangerous enterprises
very hardy and bold.   And when they are
at home in their country every one with a

stout heart defendeth his house, and surely they do it like good men and valiant captains. For if we other Romans, without reason and through ambition, do go to take another man's, it is meet and just that they by force do defend their own.

Let no man through the abundance of malice or want of wisdom envy the Roman captain, for any triumph that is given him by his mother Rome : for surely to get this, only one day's honour, he adventureth his life a thousand times in the field. I will not speak all that I might say of them that we led forth to the wars, nor of them which we leave here at home in Rome, which be all cruel judges of our fame : for their judgment is not upright according to equity, but rather proceedeth of malice and envy. Though they take me for a patient man and not far out of order, yet I let thee know, my Cornelius, that there is no patience can suffer nor heart dissemble to see many Romans to have such great envy, which (through their malicious tongue) pass not to backbite other men's triumphs. For it is an old disease of evil men, through malice to backbite that with their tongue which through their cowardice they never durst enterprise with their hands.

Notwithstanding all this ye must know, that in the war you must first often hazard your life, and afterwards to the discretion of such tongues commit your honour. Our folly is so foolish, and the desires of men so vain, that more for one vain word, than for any profit, we desire rather to get vain glory with travel, than to seek a good life with rest. And therefore willingly we offer our lives now to great travail and pain : only that among vain men hereafter we may have a name.

I swear by the immortal gods unto thee, my Cornelius, that the day of my triumph, whereas to the seeming of all those of this world I went triumphing in the chariot openly : yet I ensure thee my heart wept secretly. Such is the vanity of men, that though of reason we be admonished, called, and compelled, yet do we flee from her : and contrary, though we be rebuked, evil handled, and despised of the world, yet will we serve it. If I be not deceived it is the prosperity of foolish men, and want of good judgments that cause the men to enter into others' houses by force : rather than to be desirous to be quiet in their own with a good will. I mean that we should in following virtue sooner be virtuous, than in haunting vices, be vicious. For speaking the truth, men which in all and for all desire to please the world, must needs offer themselves to great travail and care.

O Rome, Rome, cursed be thy folly and cursed be he that in thee brought up so much pride, and be he cursed of men, and hated of Gods, which in thee hath invented this pomp. For very few are they, that worthily unto it have attained : but infinite are they, which through it have perished. What greater vanity, or what equal lightness can be, than that a Roman Captain, because he hath conquered realms, troubled quiet men, destroyed cities, beaten down castles, robbed the poor, enriched tyrants, carried away treasures, shed much blood, made infinite widows, and taken many noble men's lives, should be afterwards (with great triumph of Rome) received in recompense of all this damage ?

Wilt thou now that I tell thee a greater folly, which above all other is greatest ? I let thee wit, infinite are they that die in the wars, and one only carrieth away the glory thereof : so that these woeful and miserable men, though for their carcass they have not a grave, yet one captain goeth triumphing alone through Rome. By the immortal gods I swear unto thee, and let this pass secretly, as between friends, that the day of my triumph, when I was in my triumphant chariot, beholding the miserable captives, laden with irons, and other men carrying infinite treasures, which we had evil gotten, and to see the careful widows weep for the death of their husbands, and remembered so many noble Romans which lost their lives in Africa : though I seem to rejoice outwardly, yet I assure thee I did weep drops of blood inwardly. For he is no man born in the world, but rather a fury bred up in Hell among the furies, that can, at the sorrow of another take any pleasure.

I know not in this case what reputation the prince or captain should make of himself, that cometh from the war, and desireth to enter into Rome, for if he think (as it is reason) on the wounds he hath in his body, or the treasures which he hath wasted, on the places that he hath burnt, on the perils that he hath escaped, on the injuries which he hath received, the multitude of men which unjustly are slain, the friends which he hath lost, the enemies that he hath gotten, the little rest that he hath enjoyed, and the great travail that he hath suffered : in such case I say, that such a one with sorrowful sighs ought to lament, and with bitter tears ought to be received.

In this case of triumphing, I neither commend the Assyrians, nor envy the Persians, nor am content with the Macedonians, nor allow the Chaldeans or content me with the Greeks, I curse the Troians and condemn the Carthagians, because that they proceeded, not according to the zeal of justice but rather of the rage of pride, to set up triumphs, endamaged their countries, and left an occasion to undo us.

O cursed Rome, cursed thou hast been, cursed thou art and cursed thou shalt be. For if the fatal destinies do not lie unto me, and my judgment deceive me not, and fortune fasten not the nail, they shall see of thee Rome in time to come, that which others presently see of the realms past. Thou oughtest to know, that as thou by tyranny hast made thyself lady of lords, so by justice thou shalt return to be the servant of servants.)

O unhappy Rome, and unhappy again I return to call thee. Tell me I pray thee, why art thou at this day so dear of merchandise, and so cheap of folly ? Where are the ancient fathers which builded thee, and with their virtues honoured thee ? In whose stead presently thou magnifiest so many tyrants, which with their vices deface thee. Where are all those noble and virtuous barons which thou hast nourished, in whose stead thou hast now so many vicious and vagabonds ? Where are those, which for thy liberty did shed their blood, in whose stead now thou hast those that, to bring thee into subjection, have lost their life ? Where are thy valiant captains, which with such great travail did endeavour themselves to defend the walls from enemies, in whose stead have succeeded those that have plucked them down, and peopled them with vices, and vicious ? Where are thy great priests, they which did always pray in the temples, in whose stead have succeeded those which know not but to defile the churches, and with their wickedness to move the gods to wrath ? Where are these so many philosophers and orators, which with their counsel governed thee, in whose stead have now succeeded so many simple and ignorant, which with their malice do undo thee ?

O Rome, all those ancients have forsaken thee, and we succeed those which now are new, and if thou knewest truly the virtue of them, and didst consider the lightness of us, the day that they ended their life, the self same day not one stone in thee should have been left upon another. And so those fields should have savoured of the bones of the virtuous, which now stink of the bodies of the vicious.

Peradventure thou art more ancient than Babylon, more beautiful than Jerusalem, more rich than Carthage, more strong than Troy, more peopled than Thebes, more in circuit than Corinth, more pleasant than Tyre, more fertile than Constantinople, more high than Camena, more unvincible than

Aquileia, more privileged than Gades, more environed with towers than Capua, and more flourishing than Cantabria. We see that all those noble • cities perished, for all their virtuous defenders : and thinkest thou to remain being replenished with so much vice, and peopled with so many vicious ? O my mother Rome, take one thing for a warning, that the glory which now is of thee was first of them, and the same destruction that was of them shall hereafter light upon thee, for such is the world.

¶ For thus goeth the world, even as we presently see the troubles of them that be passed : so shall those that be to come see ours that be present.

Marcus Aurelius goeth on with his letter, and declareth the order that the Romans used in setting forth their men of war, and of the outrageous villany which captains and soldiers use in the war. [Chap. xv.]

¶ I will now declare unto thee, my friend Cornelius, the order which we have to set forth men of war : and thereby thou shalt see the great disorder that is in Rome. For in the old time there was nothing more looked unto, nor more corrected, than was the discipline of war. And for the contrary, there is nothing so dissolute as are our men of war.

News once spread abroad through the Empire how the prince doth take upon him any war, immediately divers opinions engender amongst the people, and everyone judgeth diversely upon the war. For as much as the one saith it is just, and the prince that taketh it upon him is just. Others say that it is unjust, and that the prince which began it is a tyrant. The poor and seditious persons do allow it, to the end they might go and take other men's goods by force. The rich and patient do condemn it, because they would enjoy their own in quiet. So that they do not justify or condemn war, according to the zeal of justice, but according to the little or much profit, that shall follow them of that enterprise.

I command, which am a Roman Emperor, war to be proclaimed, because a city or province hath rebelled, and that according to their custom they do not observe the ceremonies of Rome. First, you must understand, the priests must be called to go immediately to pray to the immortal gods : for the Roman people never went to shed the blood of their enemies in wars, but first the priest did shed the tears of their eyes in the temples.

¶ Secondly, all the sacred Senate doth go to the temple of the god Jupiter, and there they swear all with a solemn oath, that if the enemies (against whom they go) do require a new confederation with Rome, or demand pardon of their faults committed : that (all revengement laid on side) they shall not deny them mercy.

¶ Thirdly, the Consul which is appointed for captain of the war, went to the high Capitol, and there he maketh a solemn vow to one of the gods, which liketh him best, that he will offer him a certain jewel, if he return victorious of the same war : and though the jewel which he doth promise be of great value, yet that all people are bound to pay it.

¶ The fourth is, that they set up in the temple of Mars the ensign of the eagle, which is the ancient Roman ensign, and that is, that all the Romans take it for commandment, that no spectacle nor feast be celebrated in Rome during the time that their brethren be in the wars.

¶ The fifth, a Pretor mounteth up to the top of the gate of Salaria, and there he bloweth the trumpet to muster men of war, and they bring forth the standards and ensigns to divide them among the captains.

¶ How fearful a thing is it to see, that so soon as the captain is environed with the ensign, so soon hath he licence to commit all evils and villanies. So that he taketh it for a bravery, to rob the countries whereby he passeth, and to deceive those with whom he practiseth. What liberty captains and governors of war have to do evil, and to be evil, it is very manifest in those whom they lead in their company. For the sons leave their fathers, the servants their lords, the scholars their masters, the officers their offices, the priests their temples, the amorous their loves, and this for none other cause, but that under the colour of the liberties of war, their vices should not be punished by justice.

O, my friend Cornelius, I know not how I should begin to say that which I will tell thee. Thou oughtest to know, that after our men of war are gone out of Rome they neither fear the gods, neither honour the temples, they reverence not the priests, they have no obedience to their fathers, nor shame to the people, dread of justice, neither compassion of their country, nor remember that they are children of Rome : and yet very few of them think to end their life, but that all shame laid aside, they love the condemned idleness, and hate the just travail. Therefore heark, I will tell thee more, and though it seemeth much that I speak, I ensure thee it is but little in respect of that they do, for so much as some rob temples, others spread rumours : these break the doors, and those rob the gods. Sometimes they take the free, sometimes they loose the bond. The nights they pass in plays, the days in blasphemies, to-day they fight like Lions, to-morrow they fly like cowards. Some rebel against the captains, and others fly to the enemy. Finally, for all good they are unable, and for all evil they are meet. Therefore to tell thee of their filthiness, I am ashamed to describe them.

¶ They leave their own wives, and take the wives of others, they dishonour the daughters of the good, and they beguile the innocent Virgins : there is no neighbour but they do covet, neither hostess but that they do force, they break their old wedlock, and yearly seek a new marriage : so that they do all things what they list, and nothing what they ought. Dost thou think presently, my friend Cornelius, that there are few evils in Rome, since so many evil women do go to the war ? Here for their sake, men offend the gods, they are Traitors to their country, they deny their parentage, they do come to extreme poverty, they live in infamy, they rob the goods of others, they waste their own, they never have quiet life, neither remaineth any truth in their mouths. Finally for the love of them, often times war is moved again, and many good men lose their lives. Let us leave the reasons, and come to Histories.

¶ Thou knowest right well, that the greatest part of Asia was conquered and governed, more with the women Amazons than with any barbarous people. That young, noble,

and valiant Porro, King of Judea,[1] for want
of men, and abundance of women, was overcome of the great Alexander. Hannibal,
the terrible captain of the Carthagians, was
always lord of Italy, until he did permit
women to go to the war. And when he fell
in love with a maiden of Capua, they saw him
immediately turn his shoulders to Rome.
If Scipio the African had not scoured the
Roman armies of lechery, the invincible
Numantia had never been won. The captain
Sylla, in the wars of Mithridates, and the
courageous Marius, in the war of the Zimbres,[2]
had over their enemies so many victories,
because in their camps they suffered no
women. In the time of Claudius the Emperor,
the Tarentines and Capuans were very mortal
enemies, in so much as the one against the
other pitched their camp, and by chance one
day in the camp of the Capuans, two captains
fell at variance, because they both loved one
woman, and when the Tarentines perceived
their dissension, immediately with their
power gave them the onset.

¶ Whereof it ensueth, that through the
naughtiness of one evil woman, was lost the
liberty of that goodly city. I had in this
war of Parthes sixteen thousand horsemen,
and twenty-four thousand footmen, and
thirty-five thousand women, and the disorder

---

[1] Porus, King of India?   [2] 'Zimbres,' Cimbri.

in this case was so great, that from the host I sent my wife Faustine, and the wives of divers other Senators home to their houses, that they should keep the old and nourish the young.

¶ Our fathers led women in the old time to the war to dress meat for the whole, and to cure the wounded : but now we lead them to the end cowards should have occasion to be effeminate, and the valiant to be vicious. And in the end, their enemies do break their heads : but the women do wound their hearts.

I will that thou know other things, my Cornelius, and they are, that the Gauls, the Vulcanes, the Flaminii, the Regii, the which are priests of the mother Sibilla, of the god Vulcan, of the god Mars, and of the god Jupiter, the fear of the gods set aside, leaving their temples desert, laying of their honest garments, nor remembering their holy ceremonies, breaking their straight vows, an infinite number of them go to the camp, where they love more dishonestly than others : for it is a common thing, that those which once presumed to be solitary, and shamefast, after that they are once fleshed, exceed all others in shame and vice.

¶ It is a dishonest thing, and also perilous to carry priests to the war : for their office is to pacify the gods with tears and not to threaten men with weapons. If perchance princes would say it is good to carry priests to the war to offer sacrifices to the gods, to this I answer that the temples are built to pray, and the fields for to fight, so that in one place the gods would be feared, and in another honoured and sacrificed. In the year of the foundation of Rome 315, the Consul Vietro, passed into Asia and went against the Palestines, the which there rebelled against the Romans, and by the way he passed by the temple of Apollo, in the Isle of Delphos, and as there he made a prayer unto the god Apollo very long, to the end he would reveal unto him whether he should return victorious from Asia or not. The Oracle answered : ' O Consul Vietro, if thou wilt return victorious from thine enemies, restore our priests which thou takest from our temples : for we other gods will not that the man whom we choose for our divine service, ye others should lead to the vices of the world.' If it be true (as it is true indeed) that the god Apollo said unto the Consul Vietro, methinketh it is no just thing to condescend that priests should go to lose themselves in the war.

¶ For as thou knowest, Cornelius, without doubt greater is the offence that they commit in going to undo themselves, than is the service which they do to princes being desirous to fight.

¶ Let us have the priests in the temples to pray, and let us see how the captains are wont to govern themselves, and in this case thou shalt find that the day that the Senate do appoint a Senator for captain, they prove him if he can play at the weapons in the Theatre.

¶ The Consul leadeth him to the high Capitol with him, the eagle is hanged at his breast, they cast the purple upon his shoulders, they give him money of the common treasure, immediately he groweth into such pride that, forgetting the poverty past which he suffered in his country, he thinketh one day to make him Emperor of Rome. It is a common thing, that when fortune exalteth men of low estate to high degree they presume much and know little, and much less what they are worth. So that if their feeble force were co-equal to their high mind. one alone should suffice to overcome their enemies, and also to win many realms.

¶ The captains have taken a custom now in Rome, and they tell me it is an invention of Mauritane, that is, that they teaze their beards, they curl their hairs, they clip their words, they change their garments, they accompany with murderers, they go the most part armed, they go very fast to seem fierce, and to conclude, they little esteem to be beloved, and take it great glory to be feared.

¶ And to the intent thou shouldst know, my Cornelius, how much they would be feared, I will recite thee an history which is, that I, standing one day in Penthapolyn, a captain of mine, I hearing him and he not seeing me, for so much as they would not let him do all that he would have done in the house, he said unto an hostess of his :

¶ ' Ye other villains did never know captains of arms, therefore know it, if thou doest not know it, mother, that the earth doth never tremble but when it is threatened with a Roman Captain, and the gods do never suffer the sun to shine, but where we others are obeyed.'

¶ Since thou hast now heard that he said, hear also the valiantness that he hath done. Within short space after, the Captain went unto a battle in Arabia, where he was the first that fled, and left the standard alone in the field, the which had almost made me lose the battle.   But I, in recompense of his valiant deed, commanded to cut off his great head : for in giving the onset upon the enemies, the flying of one man doth more hurt, than the fighting of two thousand doth profit.   I have often times heard the Emperor Traian my lord say, that the men which in peace seem most fierce, in war commonly are most cowards.

¶ It chanceth that divers things are compassed for having only a good eloquence, others for having witchcraft, others for being very diligent, others for opening their purse, and truly this is the most and best mean that is occupied in Rome. But the affairs of war do not consist in talking many words before their friends : but in fighting manfully in the field against their enemies. For in the end men most full of words are for the most part cowards in deeds.

What wilt thou I tell thee more, my Cornelius, of the injuries which the captains do in the cities whereby they pass, of the slanders which they raise in the provinces where they abide ? I let thee know that the little worm doth not so much harm that gnaweth the wood, the moth to the garments, the spark unto the tow, the locusts unto the corn, neither the weevil to the garners, as the captains do to the people. For they leave no beast but they kill, nor orchard but they rob, nor wine but they drink, nor dovehouse but they climb, nor temple but they spoil, nor chase but they hunt, no sedition but they raise, no villany but that they commit. And they do more than they ought to do, for they eat without meaning to pay, and they will not serve unless they be well paid, and the worst of all is that if they have their pay, immediately they change or play it. If they be not paid, they rob and mutiny forthwith : so that with poverty they are not content, and with riches they wax vicious and insolent. The matter is now come to such corruption, and there is at this day men of war in Rome so careless, that here no captain seemeth but an example of murderers, a stirrer up of seditious persons, an envier of the good, a partaker with all evil, a thief of thieves, a pirate of rovers, and, finally, I do not say that they seem to be, but I do affirm that they are the scourge of your virtuous and refuge of the vicious. I would not say this, but yet, notwithstanding, I ought to say it because it is a thing so far out of order, and so much to be laughed at : that these wicked men though they are our familiar enemies, there is no prince that ruleth them, nor justice that correcteth them, nor fear that doth oppress them, nor law that subdueth them, nor shame that refraineth them, nor parents that correct them, nor yet death that doth end them : but now, as men which are without remedy, we let them eat of all.

Marcus Aurelius Emperor pursueth his letter, showing the great damages that have ensued for the Wars begun with strange realms.
[Chap. xvi.]

¶ O unfortunate Rome, who was not wont to have such evil luck, but the older thou art, the more unlucky I see thee. For by writ-

ings we read, and also with our eyes we see,
that the more fortunate a city or person has
been in the beginning, the more froward
fortune is unto him in the ending. Truly in
those ancient times, and in those glorious
worlds, I say when they were peopled with
true Romans, and not as now (they which
have no children but bastards), the armies
were so well taught that came from Rome,
as the philosophers which were in the schools
of Greece. If the Greek writings do not lie
unto me, Phillip the great king of Macedony,
for this is so renowned in histories, and his
son the great Alexander for this was so
fortunate in the wars, that they had their
armies so well correct, that it rather seemed
a Senate which governed, than a camp which
fought. In that we can gather out of Titus
Livius and other writers, from the time of
Quintus Cincinatus, dictator, until the noble
Marcus Marcellus were the most prosperous
times in the Roman Empire. For before
kings did travail, and afterwards it was persecuted with tyrants.

In these so happy times, one of the greatest
felicities that Rome had, was to have the
warlike discipline well corrected. And then
Rome began to fall, when our armies began
to do damage. For if those of the war have
truck with vices, the others of the common
wealth cannot have peace with virtue. O

cursed be thou Asia, and cursed be the day
that with thee we had conquest. For we
have not seen the good that has followed us
of that conquest, until this present. And
the loss and damage which from thee came
unto us, shall be lamented in Rome forever.
O cursed Asia, we spend our treasures in
thee, and thou hast given to us thy vices.
In change of our valiant men, thou hast sent
us thy fine minions, we have won thy cities,
and thou triumphest of our virtues. We
battered thy forts, and thou hast destroyed
our manners. We triumph of thy Realms,
and thou didst cut the throats of our friends.
We made to thee cruel wars, and thou con-
querest from us the good peace. With force
thou wert ours, and with good will we are
yours. We are unjust lords of thy riches,
and just tenants of thy vices. Finally, thou
Asia art a woeful grave of Rome, and thou
Rome art a filthy sink of Asia.

Since our ancient fathers did content themselves with Rome alone, why should not we
their children content ourselves with Rome
and Italy, but that we must go to conquer
Asia where we adventured our honour, and
spend our treasure? If those ancient
Romans, being as they were, so princely
barons of life, and so valiant in fighting, and
so hardy to command, did content themselves
with this little border : why should not we

content ourselves, not being as they are, having a realm rich and vicious ?

I know not what fond toy took us in the head, to go to conquer Asia, and not to content ourselves with Rome. Italy was not so poor of riches, nor so destitute of cities, nor so unpeopled of people, nor so solitary of beasts, nor so undecked with buildings, nor so barren of good fruits : but that of all these things we had more than our fathers wished, and also more than we their children deserved. For me I would say, that it is for want of judgment of abundance of pride, for us to seek to exceed our forefathers in seigniory : when we are not co-equal unto them in virtue. I was contented with all things of my forefathers, save only that they were a little proud, and seditious, and herein we their children do resemble them well.

¶ For as much as we are not only proud and seditious, but also covetous and malicious. So that in virtuous things we go backward, and in unlawful works we go forward. What is become of the great victories that our forefathers had in Asia ? What is become of the infinite treasure they have robbed in that country ? What is become of the great number of captives that they took in the war ? What is become of the strange beasts that they sent into Italy ? What is become

of the riches which everyone brought home
to his house ? What is become of the
valiant kings which they took in that conquest ? What is become of the feasts and
triumphs, wherewith they entered triumphing into Rome ? What wilt thou I say more
unto thee in this case (my Cornelius), but
that all they which invented the war are
dead, all those which were in Asia are dead,
all those which defended that country are
dead, all those which entered triumphing
into Rome are dead : and finally all the riches
and triumph which our fathers brought from
Asia, they and those in short space had an
end, except the vices and pleasures whereof
we see no end.

O, if the valiant princes knew, what a thing
it is to invent wars in strange realms, what
travails they seek for their persons, what
cares in their hearts, what trouble to their
subjects, what waste to their treasures, what
poverty to their friends, what pleasures to
their enemies, what destruction of the good,
what liberty of the evil, and what occasion
they give to strangers to speak, what univer-
sal evil they sow in their natural countries,
and what evil poison they leave to their heirs :
I swear by the faith of a good man, that if
as I feel it, princes did feel it, and as I taste it,
princes did taste it, and also as I have proved
it, princes did prove it, I do not say that with

effusion of blood I would take realms by force :
but also they offering them to me with tears,
I would not take them willingly. For speaking the truth, it is not the point of valiant
princes for to sustain another man's, to put
their own in jeopardy. I ask now, what
profit took Rome of the conquest of Asia ?
I admit that it durst conquer it, that it was
hardy in winning it, obstinate in fighting,
and happy in taking it. Should it therefore
be fortunate in maintaining it ? In this case
I say and affirm, and of that I say I do not
repent me : that it is possible to take Asia,
but it is but a folly to presume to maintain it.

¶ Dost thou not think it a great folly to
presume to maintain Asia, since there never
cometh news of a victory, but that it is
occasion of another battle, and that to sustain war they rob all Italy ? In Asia our
money is spent, our children are perished :
in Asia died our fathers, for Asia they make
us pay tributes : in Asia the good horses
are consumed : into Asia they carry all our
corn : in Asia all the thieves are nourished :
from Asia cometh all the seditious persons :
in Asia all the good do perish : from Asia
they send us all the vices : and finally in
Asia all our treasures are spent, and in Asia
all our excellent Romans are killed.

And since this is the service that Asia
doth to Rome, why will Rome continue war

with Asia ? Other princes before us have conquered Asia, taken Asia and possessed Asia : but in the end, when they saw that it was a country where they feared not the gods, nor acknowledged subjection to their princes, neither that they were apt to receive laws, they determined to forsake them : because they found by experience, that they neither weary their bodies with wars, neither win their hearts with benefits. Those princes not being hardy, nor so bold to sustain Asia by land, should we others presume to succour it by sea ? They forsake it being neighbours, and will we others maintain it being strangers ? In my opinion Asia is a country, where all the valiant men have employed their valiantness, where all the fools have proved their folly, where all the proud have showed their pride, where all the princes entered in with might, where all the tyrants have employed their life : but in the end, it neither profiteth the one to will it, nor to the others to know it, and yet much less to vanquish it.

¶ I know not the man that loveth Asia, that willeth well to Asia, that speaketh well of Asia, or that favoureth the things of Asia, since she giveth us occasion to speak daily, to sigh nightly, and to weep hourly.

¶ If men attained to the secret to know the fatal destinies, with the which the gods

have created Asia, they would not strive so
much in the conquest thereof. For the gods
have created it in such a sign, that it should
be a common pasture where all feed, a common market where all sell, a common Inn
where all rest, a common table where all play,
a common house where all dwell, a common
country where all remain : and thereof it
cometh that Asia is desired of many and
governed of few. For being as it is a common
country, every man will make it his own
proper.

¶ Peradventure thou wilt think, my
friend Cornelius, that I have spoken now
all the evils of Asia, but hearken, yet I will
form thee a new question again. For according to the damages which have followed
(from Asia) to our mother Rome, time shall
rather want to right, than matter to declare.
Not without tears I say that which I will say,
that there was never any Roman Captain
that did kill ten thousand Asians with the
weapons he brought into Asia : but that
he lost a hundred thousand Romans with
the vices they brought to Rome. So that
the Asians by the hand of their enemies
died with honour : and left us Romans alive
full of their vices with infamy. I ask now
what they were that invented to dine in
common places, to sup in secret gardens,
to apparel the women as men in the theatre,

to colour the flesh of priests with yellow, to noint the women as men in the bath, the Senators going smelling to the Senate, Princes to be apparelled with purple against the ancient decree, to eat twice in the day as the tyrant Dennis did, to keep harlots and concubines as they of Tyre do, to speak blasphemies against the gods which were never heard of before in the empire ?   These said vices of Asia, Asia hath presently sent to Rome.

¶ At the same time when in these parts of the Orient the war was kindled, ten valiant captains brought these vices to Rome, whose names my pen shall pardon to tell, because their vile offences should not obscure their valiant deeds.   Before that Rome conquered Asia we were rich, we were patient, we were sober, we were wise, we were honest, and above all, we lived contented.

¶ But since that time we have given ourselves to forget the policies of Rome, and to learn the pleasure of Asia : so that now all vices may be learned in Rome, as all sciences may be heard in Greece.

¶ By the above rehearsed, all warlike princes may see, what profit they have to conquer strange realms.   Let us now leave the vices, which in the wars are recovered, and talk of money which the princes covet and love.   And in this I say, that there is

no prince brought into so extreme poverty,
as he which conquereth a strange country.

¶ O Cornelius, thou hast not seen how
princes more of a will than of necessity do
waste their treasures : how they demand
that of another man's, and how their own
doth not suffice them : they take those of
churches, they seek great loans, they invent
great tributes, they demand great subsidies,
they give strangers occasion to speak, and
make themselves hated of their subjects.
Finally, they pray their subjects, and humble
themselves to their enemies. Since I have
declared the damages of war, I will now
declare what the original of war is.

¶ For it is impossible that the physician
apply unto the sick agreeable medicine, if
we know not of what humour the sickness
doth proceed.

¶ Princes, since they came of men, are
nourished with men, do counsel with men,
and live with men, and to conclude they
are men. Some time through pride which
aboundeth in them, some time through want
of counsel, they themselves imagine, and
other flatterers telleth, that though they have
much in respect of other princes, yet they
can do little. Also they say unto them,
that if their substance be great, their fame
ought to be greater. Further they tell them,
that the good prince ought little to esteem

that he hath inherited of his predecessors, in respect of the great deal more he ought to leave to his successors. Also they tell them, that never prince left of him any great memory, but inventing some cruel war against his enemy. Also they tell them that the hour that one is chosen Emperor of Rome, he may boldly conquer all the whole earth.

These vain reasons being heard of the princes, afterwards as their fortune is based, and their minds high, immediately they defy their enemies, they open their treasures, they assemble great armies, and in the end of all, the gods suffer that, they thinking to take another man's goods, they waste and lose their own.

O Princes, I know not who doth deceive ye, that you which by peace may be rich by war will be poor. O Princes, I know not who doth deceive you, that you which may be loved do seek occasions to be hated. O princes, I know not who doth beguile ye, that ye which may enjoy a sure life do adventure yourselves to the mutability of fortune. O Princes, I know not who doth deceive you, that you so little esteem and weigh your own abundance, and so greatly set by the want of others. O princes, I know not who doth deceive you, that all having need of you, you should have need of others.

I let thee to wit, my Cornelius, though a prince be more quick and careful than all other his predecessors have been in Rome : yet it is impossible that all things touching war should succeed unto him prosperously. For in the greatest need of war, either he wanteth money, or his subjects do not succour him, or time is contrary unto him, or he findeth perilous passages, he lacketh artillery, or the captains rebel, or else succour cometh to his adversaries : so that he seeth himself so miserable, that thoughts do more oppress his heart, than the enemies do harm his land.

Though a prince had no war, but for to suffer men of war, yet he ought to take upon him no war. I ask thee, my Cornelius, what travail so great to his person, or what greater damage to his realm can his enemies do, than that which his own men of war do ? The enemies, to do the worst they can, will but rob our frontiers : but our men of war do rob all the whole country. The enemies we dare and may resist, but to ours we cannot nor dare not speak. The enemies, the worst they can do, is once in a month to rob and run their ways : but ours daily do rob, and remain still. The enemies fear their enemies only, but ours do fear their enemies, and have no pity on their friends. The enemies, the further they go on, the more they diminish : but ours, the further they go, the more they increase.

I know no greater war that princes can have, than to have men of war in their realms. For as experience doth show us, before the gods they are culpable, to princes importunate, and to the people troublesome : so that they live to the damage of all, and to the profit of none. By the god Mars I swear unto thee (my friend Cornelius) as he may direct my hands in the war, that I have more complaints in the Senate of the thefts which my captains do commit in Illiria, than of all the enemies of the Roman people. Both for that I say, and for that I kept secret, I am more afraid to create an ensign of two hundred men of war, than to give a cruel battle to thirty thousand men. For that battle fortune (good or evil) forthwith despatcheth, but with these I can be sure no time of all my life.

Thou wilt say unto me (Cornelius) that since I am Emperor of Rome, I should remedy this since I know it. For that prince which dissembleth with the fault of another, by reason he will condemn him, as if it were his own.

To this I answer, that I am not mighty enough to remedy it, except by my remedy there should spring a greater inconvenience. And since thou hast not been a prince, thou couldst not fall into that I have, nor yet understand that which I say. For princes by their wisdom know many things, the which to remedy they have no power. So it hath been, so it is, so it shall be, so I found it, so I keep it, so will I leave it them, so I have read it in books, so have I seen it with my eyes, so I heard it of my predecessors, and finally I say, so our fathers have invented it, and so will we the children sustain it, and for this evil, we will leave it to our heirs.

I will tell thee one thing, and imagine that I err not therein, which is, considering the great damage, and little profit, which the men of war do bring to our common wealth, I think to do it, and to sustain it, either it is the folly of men, or a scourge given of the gods. For there can be nothing more just, than for the gods to permit, that we feel that in our own houses, which we cause others in strange houses to lament.

All those things I have written unto thee, not for that it skilleth greatly that thou know them : but that my heart is at ease to utter them. For as Alcibiades said, ' The chests and the hearts ought always to be open to their friends.' Panutius my secretary, goeth in my behalf to visit that land, and I gave him this letter to give thee, with two horses, wherewith I think you will be contented, for they are jennets. The weapons and riches which I took of the Parthes I have now divided, notwithstanding I do send thee two chariots of them. My wife Faustine greeteth thee, and I send a rich glass for thy daughter, and a jewel with stones for thy sister. No more but I beseech the gods to give thee a good life, and me a good death.

III

Of a letter of the Emperor Marcus Aurelius, to Claudius and Claudinus, reproving them being old men, for that they lived youthfully. [Chap. xix.]

¶ Mark Emperor, born in Mount Celio, desireth to you my neighbours, Claude and Claudine, health of your persons, and amendment of your lives.

I being as I am, at the conquest of Asia, and you remaining always in the pleasures of Rome, we understand your news very late, and I think our letters arrive there as late. Notwithstanding to all those which go thither, I give answers for you others : and of all those which come hither, I demand of your health. And do not demand of others, how well and how much I love you, but of your own proper hearts : and if your hearts say that I am a feigned friend, then I take myself condemned. If perchance your hearts do tell you that I love you, being true in deed that I hate you, or if I tell you that I hate you, being true that I love you : of truth I would pluck such a heart out of my body, and give it to be eaten of the beasts. For there is no greater deceit, than that which the man doth to himself. If a stranger beguile me, I ought to dissemble it : if an enemy deceive me, I ought to revenge it : if my friend misuse me, I ought to complain of him : but if I do deceive myself, with whom shall I comfort myself ? For there is no patience that can suffer the heart to deceive himself in anything, which he hath not deeply considered.

Peradventure ye will say that I do not esteem you, and that I have not written any letter unto you of long time. To this I answer, that you do not attribute the fault to my negligence, but to the great distance of countries that there is from hence to Rome : and also to the great affairs of Asia. For amongst other discommodities the war hath this also, that it depriveth us of the sweet conversation of our country.

I have always presumed to be yours, and at this present am at no man's pleasure more than at yours. And since you have always known of me, what you desired to know, I have espied in you others that which of force I must speak. For in the end I have not seen any possess so much, to be worth so much, to know so much, nor in all things to be so mighty, but that one day he should need his poor friend. The divine Plato said, and also well, that the man which loveth with his heart, neither in absence forgetteth, neither in presence becometh negligent, neither in prosperity he is proud, nor yet in adversity abject, neither he serveth for profit, nor yet he loveth for gain : and finally he defendeth the case of his friend as his own.

Divers have been of the opinions which the ancients held to affirm for what end friends were taken, and in the end they were fully resolved, that for four causes we ought to choose friends.

The first, we ought to have friends to treat and to be conversant with all, for according to the troubles of this life, there is no time so pleasantly consumed, as in the conversation of an assured friend.

The second is, we ought to have friends to whom we may disclose the secrets of our hearts : for it is much comfort to the woeful heart to declare to his friend his doubts, if he perceive that he doth feel them indeed.

The third, we ought to search and choose friends, to the end they help us in our adversities. For little profiteth it my heart that with tears the friends do hear all that

I bewail, unless afterwards in deed he will take pains to reform the same.

¶ The fourth, we ought to seek and preserve friends to the end they be protectors of our goods, and likewise, judges of our evils: for the good friend is no less bound to withdraw us from the vices whereby we are slandered, than to deliver us from our enemies, by whom we may be slain.

The end where I told you all this was, if that in this letter you chance to light of any sharp word, that you take it patiently, considering that the love which I bear you doth move me to speak, and the faith which I owe unto you, doth not suffer me that I should keep it close. For many things ought to be borne among friends, though they tell them in earnest : which ought not to be suffered of others, though they speak it in jest. I come therefore to show the matter, and I beseech the immortal gods that there be no more than that which was told me, and that it be less than I suspect.

Gaius Furius, your kinsman and my especial friend, as he went to the realm of Palestine and Jerusalem, came to see me in Antioch, and hath told me news of Italy and Rome, and among others one above all the residue I have committed to memory, at the which I could not refrain laughing, and less to be troubled after I had thought

of it. O how many things do we talk in jest,
the which after we have well considered give
occasion to be sorry. The Emperor Adrian,
my good lord, had a jester whose name was
Belphus, young, comely, and stout, albeit
he was very malicious as such are accustomed
to be : and whilst the ambassadors of Germany supped with the Emperor in great
joy, the same Belphus began to jest of every
one that was present, according to his accustomed manner with a certain malicious
grace. And Adrian perceiving that some
changed colour, others murmured, and others
were angry, he said unto this jester, ' Friend
Belphus, if thou love me and my service,
use not those spiteful jests at our supper,
which being considered on, may turn us to
evil rest in our beds.' Gaius Furius hath
told me so many slanders chanced in Italy,
such novelties done in Rome, such alteration
of our Senate, such contention and strife
between our neighbours, such lightness of
you two, that I was astonied to hear it, and
ashamed to write it. And it is nothing to
tell after what sort he told them unto me,
unless you had seen how earnestly he spake
them, imagining that as he told them without
taking any pain, so did I receive them (as
he thought) without any grief : though
indeed every word that he spake seemed a
sharp piercing arrow unto my heart. For

ofttimes some telleth us things, as of small importance, the which do prick our hearts to the quick.

By the opinion of all, I understand that you are very old, and yet in your own fantasies, you seem very young. And further they say, you apparel yourselves anew now, as though presently you came into the world : and moreover they say that you are offended with nothing so much, as when they call you old, and that in theatres where comedies are played, and in the fields where the brute beasts do run, you are not the hindmost, and that there is no sport nor lightness invented in Rome, but first is registered in your house. And finally they say that you give yourselves so to pleasures, as though you never thought to receive displeasures.

O Claude and Claudine, by the god Jupiter I swear unto you, that I am ashamed of your unshamefastness, I am greatly abashed of your manners, and above all, I am exceedingly grieved for your great offence. For at that time that you ought to lift your hands, you are returned again into the filth of the world. Many things men commit, which though they seem grave, yet by moderation of the person that committeth them are made light, but speaking according to the truth, I find one reason whereby I might excuse your lightness, but to the contrary I see ten whereby I may condemn your follies.

Solon, the philosopher, in his laws said to the Athenians, that if the young offended he should be gently admonished and grievously punished, because he was strong: and if the old did err, he should be lightly punished, and sharply admonished, since he was weak and feeble. To this Licurgus, in his laws to the Lacedemonians said contrary, that if the young did offend, he should be lightly punished and grievously admonished, since through ignorance he did err: and the old man which did evil, should be light admonished and sharply punished, since through malice he did offend. These two philosophers being (as they have been) of such authority in the world that is past, and considering that their laws and sentences were of such weight: it should be much rashness in not admitting the one of them. Now not receiving the one, nor reproving the other, me thinketh that there is great excuse to the young for their ignorance, and great condemnation to the aged for their experience.

Once again I return to say that you pardon me, my friends, and you ought not greatly to weigh it, though I am somewhat sharp in condemnation, since you others are so dissolute in your lives: for of your black life my pen doth take ink. I remember well

that I have heard of thee, Claude, that thou
hast been lusty and courageous in thy youth :
so that thy strength of all was envied, and
the beauty of Claudine of all men was desired. I will not write unto you in this
letter, my friends and neighbours, neither
reduce to memory how thou, Claude, hast
employed thy forces in the service of the
commonwealth, and thou, Claudine, hast
won much honour of thy beauty : for sundry
times it chanced, that men of many goodly
gifts are noted of grievous offences. Those
which strived with thee are all dead, those
whom thou desirest are dead, those which
served thee, Claudine, are dead, those which
before thee, Claudine, sighed, are dead: those
which for thee died, are now dead : and since
all those are dead with their lightness, do not
you others think to die, and your follies also ?

I demand now of thy youth one thing, and
of thy beauty another thing. What do you
receive of these pastimes, of these good
entertainments, of these abundances, of these
great contentations of the pleasures of the
world, of the vanity that is past, and what
hope you of all these to carry into the narrow
grave ? O simple, simple, and ignorant persons, how our life consumeth, and we perceive not how we live therein. For it is no
felicity to enjoy a short or long life : but to
know to employ the same well, or evil. O

children of the earth and disciples of vanity, now you know that time flyeth without moving his wings, that life goeth without lifting up his feet, the world despatcheth us not telling the cause, men beguile us not moving their lips, our flesh consumeth to us unawares, the heart dieth having no remedy, and finally, our glory decayeth as if it had never been, and death oppresseth us without knocking at the door. Though a man be never so simple, or so very a fool : yet he cannot deny but it is impossible to make a fire in the bottom of the sea, to make a way in the air, of the thin blood to make rough sinews, and of the soft veins to make hard bones. I mean, that it is impossible that the green flower of youth be not one day withered by age.

¶ *The Emperor followeth his letter and persuadeth Claudius and Claudinus being now old to give no more credit to the world nor to any of his deceitful flatteries.*

[Chap. xx.]

¶ That which I have spoken now, tendeth more to advertise the young, than to teach the old. For you others have now passed the prime time of childhood, the summer of youth, and the harvest of adolescency, and are in the winter of age, where it seemeth an uncomely thing, that those your hoary hairs should be accompanied with such vain follies. Since young men know not that they have to end their youth, it is no marvel that they follow the world : but the old men which see themselves fall into this guile, why will they run after vices again ?

O world, for that thou art the world, so small is our force, and so great our debility, that thou willing it, and we not resisting it, thou dost swallow us up in the most perilous gulf, and in the thorns most sharp thou dost prick us : by the priviest ways thou leadest us, and by the most stony ways thou carriest us. I mean that thou bringest us to the highest favours, to the end that afterwards, with a push of thy pike, thou mightest overthrow us.

O world, wherein all is worldly, two and fifty years have passed since in thee I was first born, during which time thou never toldest me one truth : but I have taken thee with ten thousand lies. I never demanded the thing but thou didst promise it me, and yet it is nothing at all that ever thou didst perform. I never put my trust in thee, but ever thou beguiledst me, I never came to thee but thou didst undo me, finally, never saw I ought in thee whereby thou deservest love, but always hatred.

This presupposed, I know not what is in

thee, O world, or what we worldlings want : for if thou hatest us we cannot hate thee, if thou dost us injury, we can dissemble it, if thou spurn us with thy feet we will suffer it, if thou beatest us with a staff, we will hold our peace, also although thou persecutest us, we will not complain, though you take ours, we will not demand it of thee, though thou dost beguile us we will not call ourselves beguiled, and the worst of all is that thou dost chase us from thy house, yet we will not depart from thence.

I know not what this meaneth, I know not from whence this cometh : I know not who ought to praise this same that we covet to follow the world which will none of us, and hate the gods which love us. Oft times I make account of my years past, sometimes also I turn and toss my book to see what I have read, and another time I desire my friends to give me good counsel : and for no other end I do it, than to attain to that I have spoken, and to know that I will say.

I reading Rhetoric in Rhodes, Adrian, my lord, maintaining me there, knowing that I was two and thirty years of age, it happened that in the spring time I found my life solitarily, and solitariness with liberty smelled the world, and smelling it I knew it, and knowing it I followed it, and following it I attained unto it, and attaining unto it, thereunto I joined myself, and joining myself therewith I proved it, and in proving it I tasted it, and in tasting it methought it bitter, and in finding it bitter I hated it, and hating it I left it, and leaving it is returned, and being returned I received it again: finally, the whole world inviting me, and I not resisting it, two and fifty years we did eat our bread together, and in one house we have always remained. Wilt thou know after what sort the world and I do live in one house together, or better to say, in one heart remain? Hearken then, and in one word I will tell it thee.

When I saw the world brave, I served him: when he saw me sad he flattered me: when I saw him wealthy, I asked him: when he saw me merry, he beguiled me: when I desired anything, he holp me to attain it, and afterwards when the same I best enjoyed, then he took it from me: when he saw me not pleased, he visited me: when he saw me, he forgot me: when he saw me overthrown, he gave me his hand to relieve me: when he saw me exalted, he tripped me again to overthrow me. Finally, when I think that I have somewhat in the world, I find that all that I have is a burden.

If this which I have spoken of the world be anything, more is that a great deal which yet of myself I will say, which is, that without doubt my folly is greater than his malice, since I am beguiled so oft, and yet always I follow the deceiver. O world, world, thou hast such moods and passions in thy proceeding, that thou leadest us all to perdition.

Of one thing I marvel much, whereof I cannot be satisfied. Which is, since that we may go upon the bridge and yet without any gain we do wade through the water, and whereas the shallow is sure, we seek to run into the gulf, and where the way is dry, we go into the splash, where we may eat wholesome meat to nourish the life, we receive poison to hasten death, we seek to destroy ourselves, whereas we may be without danger. Finally I say, without profit we commit a fault, though we see with our eyes the pain to follow.

Wise men ought circumspectly to see what they do, to examine that they speak, to prove that they take in hand, to beware whose company they use, and above all, to know whom they trust. For our judgment is so corrupt, that to beguile us, one is enough : and to make us not to be deceived, ten thousand would not suffice. They have so great care of us, I mean the world to beguile us and the flesh to flatter us, that the highway being as it is narrow, the pathway dangerous and full of pricks, the journey is long and the life short : our bodies are never but laden with vices and our hearts but full of cares.

I have wondered at divers things in this world, but that which astonisheth me most is that those that be good, we make them believe they are evil, and those which are evil, we persuade others to believe that they are good. So that we shoot at the white of virtues, and hit the butt of vices.

I will confess one thing, the which being disclosed, I know that infamy will follow me, but peradventure some virtuous man will marvel at it, that is, that in those two and fifty years of my life, I have proved all the vices of this world, for no other intent, but for to prove if there be anything wherein man's malice might be satisfied. And afterwards, all well considered, all examined and all proved, I find that the more I eat, the more I die for hunger, the more I drink, the greater thirst I have, the more I rest, the more I am broken, the more I sleep, the more drowsy I am, the more I have, the more I covet, the more I desire, the more I am tormented, the more I procure, the less I attain. Finally, I never had so great pain through want, but afterwards I had more trouble with excess.

It is a great folly to think that as long as a man liveth in this flesh, that he can satisfy

the flesh : for at the last cast, she may take
from us our life, but we others cannot take
from her her disordinate covetousness.   If
men did speak with the gods, or the gods
were conversant with men, the first thing
that I would ask them should be, why they
have appointed an end to our woeful days,
and will not give us an end of our wicked
desires ?   O cruel gods, what is it you do ?
Or what do you suffer us ?   It is certain that
we shall not pass one good day of life only,
but in tasting this and that, life consumeth.
O intolerable life of man, wherein there are
such malices from the which we ought to
beware, and such perils to fall in, and also
so many things to consider, that then both she
and we do end to know ourselves, when the
hour of death approacheth.   Let those know
that know not, that the world taketh our
will and we others like ignorants cannot
deny it him, and afterwards, having power
of our will, doth constrain us to that which
we would not : so that many times we would
do virtuous works, and for that we are now
put into the world's hands, we dare not do it.

The world useth another subtlety with
us, that to the end we should not strive with
it, it praiseth the times past, because we
should live according to the time present.
And the world saith further that if we others
employ our forces in his vices, he giveth us

licence that we have a good desire of virtue.
O would to God in my days I might see, that
the care which the world hath to preserve
us, the worldlings would take it to withdraw
them from his vices. I swear that the gods
should then have more servants, and the
world and the flesh should not have so many
slaves.

¶ *The Emperor proceedeth in his letter, and
proveth by good reasons, that since the
aged persons will be served and honoured
of the young, they ought to be more virtuous and honest than the young.*

[Chap. xxi.]

¶ I have spoken all this before rehearsed,
for occasion of you, Claude and Claudine, the
which at three score and ten years will not
keep out of the prison of the world. You I
say, which have your bodies weak and corrupted, what hope shall we have of young
men which are but twenty-five years of age ?
If my memory deceive me not, when I was
there you had nephews married, and of
their children made sure, and two of the
children born : and since that is true, methinketh when the fruit is gathered, the leaf
is of no value, and after the meal is taken
from the mill, evil shall the mill grind.

¶ I mean, that the old man ought to

desire that his days might be shortened in this world. Do not think, my friends, that a man can have his house full of nephews, and yet say that he is very young, for in loading the tree with fruit, the blossoms immediately fall or else they become withered. I have imagined with myself what it is that you might do to seem young, and cut off some of your years : and in the end I know no other reason but when you married Alamberta your daughter with Drusus, and your niece Sophia the fair with Tuscidan, which were so young, that the daughters were scarce fifteen years old, nor the young men twenty. I suppose because you were rich of years and poor of money, that he gave to every one of them, instead of money for dowry, twenty years of yours : hereof a man may gather, that the money of your nephews have remained unto you, and you have given unto them of your own years.

I understand, my friends, that your desire is to be young, and very young, but I greatly desire to see you old, and very old. I do not mean in years, which in you doth surmount : but in discretion which in you doth want. O Claude and Claudine, note that which I will say unto you, and bear it always in your memory. I let you wit, that to maintain youth, to deface age, to live contented, to be free from travails, to lengthen life, and to avoid death, these things are not in the hands of men which do desire them, but rather in the hands of those which giveth them : the which, according to their justice, and not to our covetousness, do give us life by weight, and death without measure.

One thing the old men do which is cause of slandering many, that is, that they will speak first in counsel, they will be served of the young in feasts, they will be first placed, in all that they say they will be believed, in churches they will be higher than the residue, in distributing of offices they will have the most honour, in their opinions they will not be gainsaid, finally, they will have the credit of old sage men, and yet they will lead the life of young doting fools. All these pre-eminences and privileges, it is very just that old men should have [1] spent their years in the service of the common wealth : but with this I do advise and require them, that the authority given them with their white hairs be not diminished by their evil works.

¶ Is it a just thing, that the humble and honest young man do reverence to the aged man proud and disdainful ? Is it a just thing, that the gentle and gracious young man do reverence to the envious and mali-

[1] Query : 'should have that have.'

cious old man ? Is it a just thing, that the
virtuous and patient young man do reverence to the foolish and unpatient old man ?
Is it a just thing, that the stout and liberal
young man do reverence to the miserable
and covetous old man ? Is it just, that the
diligent and careful young man do reverence
to the negligent old man ? Is it just, that
the abstinent and sober young man do
reverence to the greedy and gluttonous old
man ? Is it just, that the chaste and continent young man do reverence to the lech-
erous and dissolute old man ? Methinkest
these things should not be such, that thereby
the old man should be honoured : but rather
reproved and punished. For old men offend
more, by the evil example they give, than by
the fault which they do commit.

Thou canst not deny me, my friend
Claude, that it is thirty and three years
since we both were at the Theatres to behold
a play, when thou camest late, and found
no place for thee to sit in, thou saidst unto
me who was set : ' Rise, my son Mark, and
since now thou art young, it is but just that
thou give me place which am aged.' If it
be true that it is three and thirty years since
thou askest place in the theatre as an old
man, tell me I pray thee, and also I conjure
thee, with what ointment hast thou anointed
thyself, or with what water hast thou

washed thyself to become young ? O Claude, if thou hast found any medicine, or discovered any herb, wherewith thou couldst take white hairs from men's heads, and from women the wrinkles of their face : I swear unto thee, and also do I assure thee, thou shouldst be more visited and served in Rome, than the god Apollo is in his temple at Ephesus. Thou shouldst well remember Annius Priscus, the old man which was our neighbour and somewhat akin to thee, the which when I told him that I could not be filled with his good words, and to behold his ancient white hairs, he said unto me : ' O my son Mark, it appeareth well that thou hast not been aged, because thou talkest as a young man : for if white hairs do honour the person, they greatly hurt the heart : for at that hour when they see us aged, the strangers do hate us, and ours do not love us.' And he told me more : ' I let thee know, my son Mark, that many times my wife and I talking of the years of another particularly, when she beholdeth me, and that I seem unto her so aged, I say unto her and swear that I am yet young, and that the white hairs came unto me by great travails, and the age by sickness.'

I do remember also, that this Annius Priscus was Senator one year : and because he would not seem aged, and desired that men should judge him to be young, he shaved his beard and his head, which was not customary among the Senators nor Censors of Rome. And as one day amongst other Senators he entered into the high Capitol, one said unto him : ' Tell me, man, from whence comest thou ? what wilt thou and why comest thou hither ? How durst thou being no Senator enter into the Senate ? ' He answered : ' I am Annius Priscus the aged, how chanceth it that now you have not known me ? ' They replied unto him, ' If thou wert Annius Priscus thou wouldst not come thus shaven. For in this sacred Senate can none enter to govern the commonwealth, unless his person be endowed with virtues, and his head with white hairs, and therefore thou art banished and deprived of thy office, for the old which live as the young ought to be punished.'

Thou knowest well, Claude and Claudine, that that which I have spoken is not the feigning of Homer, neither a fable of Ouid, but that you yourselves saw it with your eyes, and in his banishment I did help him with money, and moreover he was banished another time for the lightness he did commit in the night in the city, and I marvel not hereof : for we see by experience that old men which are steeped in vices, are more obstinate to correct than the young. O what evil fortune have the old men, which suffered themselves to wax old in vices : for more danger is the fire in an old house than in a new, and a great cut of a sword is not so perilous as a rotten fistula. Though old men were not honest and virtuous, for the service of the gods and the commonwealth, for the saying of the people, nor for the example of the young : yet he ought to be honest, if it were but for the reverence of their years. If the poor old man have no teeth, how shall he eat ? If he have no heat in his stomach, how can he digest ? If he have no taste, how can he drink ? If he be not strong, how can he be an adulterer ? If he have no feet, how can he go ? If he have the palsy, how can he speak ? If he have the gout in his hands, how can he play ? Finally, suchlike worldly and vicious men have employed their forces, being young, desirous to prove all these vices : and when they are old it grieveth them extremely that they cannot as yet accomplish their desires.

¶ Amongst all the faults in old men (in my opinion) this is the chiefest, that since they have proved all things, that they should still remain in their obstinate folly. There is no part but they have travelled, no villany but they have essayed, no fortune but they have proved, no good but they have persecuted, no evil but hath chanced unto them, nor there is any vice but they have attempted. These unhappy men, which in this sort have spent all their youth, have in the end their combs cut with infirmities and diseases : yet they are not so much grieved with the vices (which in them do abound) to hinder them from virtues, as they are tormented for want of corporal courage, to further them in their lusts. O if we were gods, or that they would give us licence to know the thoughts of the old, as we see with our eyes the deeds of the young : I swear to the god Mars, and also to the mother Berecinthia, that without comparison, we would punish more the wicked desires which the aged have to be wicked, than the light deeds of the young.

Tell me, Claude, and thou, Claudine, do you think, though you behave yourselves as young, you shall not seem to be old ? Know you not that our nature is the corruption of our body and that our body hindereth our understandings, and that the understandings are kept of our soul, and that our soul is the mother of desires, and that our desires are the scourge of our youth, and that our youth is the ensign of our age, and age the spy of death, and that death in the end is the house where life taketh his harbour, and from whence youth flyeth a-foot, and from whence age cannot escape a-horseback ?

I would rejoice that you, Claude and Claudine, would tell me what you find in life that so much therewith you should be contented : since now you have passed four score years of life, during the which time, either you have been wicked in the world, or else you have been good. If you have been good, ye ought to think it long until you be with the good gods : if you have been evil, it is just you die to the end that you be no worse. For speaking the truth those which in three score and ten years have been wicked in works, leave small hope of their amendment of life.

Adrian, my lord, being at Nola in Campania, one brought unto him a nephew of his from the study, whereas the young child had not profited a little, for he became a great Grecian and Latinist, and moreover he was fair, gracious, wise, and honest. And this Emperor Adrian loved his nephew so much, that he said unto him these words, ' My nephew, I know not whether I ought to say unto thee that thou art good or evil : for if thou be evil, life shall be evil employed on thee, and if thou be good, thou oughtest to die immediately, and because I am worse than all, I live longer than all.'

These words which Adrian, my lord, said do plainly declare and express, that in short space the pale and cruel death doth assault the good, and lengtheneth life a great while to the evil. The opinion of a philosopher was that the gods are so profound in their secrets, high in their mysteries, and so just in their works, that to men which least profit the common wealth they lengthen life longest: and though he had not said it, we others see it by experience. For the man which is good, and that beareth great zeal and friendship to the common wealth, either the gods take him from us, or the enemies do slay him, or the dangers do cast him away, or the travails do finish him.

When great Pompeius and Julius Cæsar became enemies and from that enmity came to cruel wars, the chronicles of that time declare that the kings and people of that occidental part became in the favour of Julius Cæsar, and the mightiest and most puissant of all the Oriental parts came in the aid of great Pompeius, because these two princes were loved of few, and served and feared of all. Amongst the diversity and sundry nations of people which came out of the Oriental part into the host of the great Pompeius, one nation came marvellous cruel and barbarous, which said they dwelled in the other side of the mountains Riphees which go unto India. And these barbarians had a custom, not to live no longer than fifty years, and therefore when they came to that age they made a great fire and were burned therein alive, and of their own wills they sacrificed themselves to the gods. Let no man be astonied at that we have spoken, but rather let them marvel of that we will speak (that is to say) that the same day that any man had accomplished fifty years, immediately he cast himself quick into the fire, and the parents, children, and his friends made a great feast. And the feast was, that they did eat the flesh of the dead half burned, and drank in wine and water the ashes of his bones : so that the stomach of the children being alive, was the grave of the fathers being dead.

All this that I have spoken with my tongue, Pompeius hath seen with his eyes, for that some being in the camp did accomplish fifty years, and because the case was strange, he declared it oft times in the Senate.

Let every man judge in this case what he will and condemn the barbarous at his pleasure, yet I will not cease to say what I think. O golden world, which had such men, O blessed people, of whom in the world to come shall be a perpetual memory. What contempt of world ! What forgetfulness of himself ! What stroke of fortune ! What whip for the flesh ! What little regard of life ! O what bridle for the virtuous ! O what confusion for those that love life ! O how great example have they left us not to fear death! Since those here have willingly despised their own lives, it is not to be thought that they died to take the goods of others, neither to think that our life should never have end, nor our covetousness in like manner. O glorious people, and ten thousandfold happy that the proper sensuality being forsaken, have overcome the natural appetite to desire to live, not believing in that they saw, and that having faith in that they never saw, they strived with the fatal destinies. By the way they assaulted fortune, they changed life for death, they offered the body to death and above all have won honour with the gods, not for that they should hasten death, but because they should take away that which is superfluous of life. Archagent, a surgeon of Rome, and Antonius Musus, a physician of the Emperor Augustus, and Esculapius, father of the physic, should get little money in that country. He that then should have sent to the barbarous to have done as the Romans of that time did, that is to say, to take syrups in the mornings, pills at night, to drink milk in the morning, to anoint themselves with gromelseed, to be let blood to-day and purged to-morrow, to eat of one thing and to abstain from many : a man ought to think that he which willingly seeketh death will not give money to lengthen life.

¶ *The Emperor concludeth his letter and showeth what perils those old men live in which dissolutely like young children pass their days, and giveth unto them wholesome counsel for the remedy thereof.*

[Chap. xxii.]

¶ But returning now to thee, Claude, and to thee, Claudine, me thinketh that these barbarous, being fifty years of age, and you others having above three score and ten, it should be just that, since you were older in years, you were equal in virtue, and though (as they) you will not accept death patiently : yet at the least, you ought to amend your evil lives willingly.

I do remember that it is many years since that Fabritius the young, son of Fabritius the old, had ordained to have deceived me, of the which if you had not told me, great inconveniences had happened : and since that you did me so great a benefit, I would now requite you the same with another like. For amongst friends there is no equal benefit, than to deceive the deceiver. I let you know, if you do not know it, that you are poor aged folks, your eyes are sunk into your heads, the nostrils are shut, the hairs are white, the hearing is lost, the tongue faltereth, the teeth fall, the face is wrinkled, the feet

swollen, and the stomach cold. Finally I
say, that if the grave could speak as unto his
subjects, by justice he might command you
to inhabit his house.

It is a great pity of the young men, and
of their youthful ignorance, for then unto
such their eyes are not opened, to know the
mishaps of this miserable life, when cruel
death doth end their days, and adjourneth
them to the grave. Plato in his book of the
commonwealth said, that in vain we give
good counsels to fond and light young men :
for youth is without experience of that it
knoweth, suspicious of that it heareth, in-
credible of that is told him, despising the
counsel of another and very poor of his own.
For so much as this is true that I tell you,
Claude and Claudine, that without comparison, the ignorance which the young have of
the good is not so much : but the obstination
which the old hath in the evil is more. For
the mortal gods many times do dissemble
with a thousand offences committed by
ignorance, but they never forgive the offence
perpetrated by malice.

O Claude and Claudine, I do not marvel
that you do forget the gods (as you do) which
created you, and your fathers which begot
you, and your parents which have loved you,
and your friends which have honoured you :
but that which most I marvel at is that you

forget yourselves. For you never consider what you ought to be, until such time as you be there where you would not be and that without power to return back again. Awake, awake, since you are drowned in your dreams, open your eyes since you sleep so much, accustom yourselves to travels, since you are vagabonds, learn that which behoveth you, since now you are so old. I mean, that in time convenient, you agree with death before he make execution of life.

Fifty-two years have I known the things of the world, and yet I never saw a woman so aged through years, nor old man with members so feeble, that for want of strength could not (if they list) do good : nor yet for the same occasion should leave to be evil if they list to be evil. It is a marvellous thing to see, and worthy to note, that all the corporal members of man waxeth old, but the inward heart, and the outward tongue : for the heart is always given to invent evils, and the tongue is always able to tell lies.

My opinion should be that the pleasant summer being past, you should prepare yourselves for the untemperate winter which is at hand. And if you have but few days to continue, you should make haste to take up your lodging. I mean that, since you have passed the days of your life with travel, you should prepare yourselves against the night of death, to be in the haven of rest.   Let mockeries pass as mockeries, and accept truth as truth, that is to wit, that it were a very just thing, and also for your honour necessary, that all those which in times past have seen you young and foolish, should now in your age see you grave and sage.   For there is nothing that so much forgetteth the lightness and folly of the youth, as doth gravity and constancy in age.   When the knight runneth his career, they blame him not for that the horse mane is not finely combed: but at the end of his race he should see his horse amended and looked to.

What greater confusion can be to any person, or greater slander to our mother Rome, than to see that which nowadays therein we see, that is to wit, the old which can scarcely creep through the streets, to behold the plays and games as young men, which search nought else but pomp and vanity.   It grieveth me to speak it, but I am much more ashamed to see, that the old Romans do daily cause the white hairs to be plucked out of their heads because they would not seem old, to make their beards small to seem young, wearing their hose very close, their shirts open before, the gown of the Senator embroidered, the Roman sign richly enamelled, the collar of gold at the neck, as those of Dace, fringes in their gowns, as those of Saphire, hoops in their hats, as the Greeks, and pearls on their fingers, as those of India. What wilt thou I tell thee more than I have told thee, but that they wear their gowns long and large, as those of Tarenthe, and they wear them of the colour as men of war, and every week they have change as players, and the worst of all is, that they show themselves as doting in love now in their age, as others have done heretofore in their youth. That old men are overcome by young desires, I do not marvel, for that brutish lust is as natural as the daily food : but that old men (being old men) should be so dissolute, herewith men justly ought to be offended. For the old men covetous, and of flesh vicious, both offend the gods, and slander the commonwealth.

O how many I have known in Rome, who in their youth have been highly praised and esteemed and afterwards, through giving themselves so very much lightness in their age, have been of all abhorred. And the worst of all is, that they have lost all their credit, their parents their favour, and their poor innocent children their profit. For many times the gods permit that the fathers committing the offence the pain should fall upon their own children.

The renowned Gaguino Cato, who descended from the high lineage of the sage Catoes, was

five years Flamen priest, and administrator
to the vestal virgins, three years Pretor, two
years Censor, one year Dictator and five
times Consul, being 75 years old he gave himself to follow, serve, and to desire Rosana,
the daughter of Gneus Cursius, a lady of
truth very young and fair, and of many
desired, and much made of. Time afterwards passing away, and god Cupid doing
his office, the love was so kindled inwardly
in the heart of this old man, that he ran
almost mad : so that after he had consumed all his goods in serving her, daily
he sighed, and nightly he wept, only for to
see her.

It chanced that the said Rosana fell sick
of a burning ague, wherewith she was so
distempered that she could eat no meat, but
desired greatly to eat grapes : and since
there were none ripe at Rome, Gaguino Cato
sent to the river of Rhine to fetch some,
being far and distant many miles from thence.
And when the thing was spread through
Rome, and that all the people knew it, the
Senate understanding the folly of him, the
fathers commanded that Rosana should be
locked up with the vestal virgins, and the
old man banished Rome for ever, to the end
that to them it should be a punishment, and
to others an example. Truly it grieved me
sore to see it, and also I have great pains in

writing it. For I saw the father die in infamy, and his children live in poverty.

I believe that all those which shall hear this example, and all those which shall read this writing, shall find the fact of this amorous old man both vile and filthy, and they will allow the sentence of the Senate which they gave against him for good and just. I swear that if Gaguino Cato had had as many young men in his banishment as he left old men lovers that followed his example in Rome, there should not be cast away so many men neither so many women evil married.

It chanceth oft times that when the old men (specially being noble, and valiant) are advertised of their servants, are rebuked of their parents, are praised of their friends, and accused of their enemies to be dishonest, in such a place they answer, that they are not in love, but in jest. When I was very young no less in wisdom than in age, one night in the Capitol I met with a neighbour of mine, the which was so old that he might have taken me for his nephew, to whom I said these words : ' Lord Fabricus, are you also in love ? ' He answered me, ' You see that my age suffereth me not that I should be a lover, if I should be, it is but in sport.'

¶ Truly, I marvelled to meet him at that hour and I was ashamed to have such an answer. In old men of great age and gravity such request cannot be called love but grief, not pastime, but loss of time, not mockery, but villany. For of love in jest ensueth infamy in deed. I ask you, Claude and Claudine, what a thing is it to see an old man to be in love ? Truly, it is no other but as a garland laid before the tavern doors, where all men think there is wine, and they sell nought else but vinegar. They are eggs white without and rotten within : they are golden pills, the taste whereof are very bitter, and as empty boxes in shops which have new writings on them, or as a new gate, and within the house is full of filth and cobwebs. Finally, that old lover is a knight of Erchetes, which helpeth to lose many, and can deliver no man from peril. Let this word be noted and always in your memory committed, that the old man which is vicious is but as a leek which hath the head white and the tail green.

Me thinketh that you ought to break the wings of time, since that you have feathers to fly withal. Deceive not yourself nor your friends and neighbours, saying that there is time for all. For the amendment is in your hands, but time is in the hands of God to dispose.

Let us come now to remedy this great damage. Do what you can by the day of youth, and defer it not until the night of age, for ill cutteth the knife, when the edge thereof is dulled, and ill can he gnaw the bones which is accustomed to eat the flesh. I tell you and advertise you that when old and rotten houses begin to fall, underset them not with rotten wood, but with hard timber. I mean, with the upright thoughts of accounts, which we ought to give to the gods of our life, and to men of our renown. For I say that if the vine be gathered of our virtues, we ought to graff again the amendment : and if the shreds of our gatherings be dry and withered, through our perverse works, we ought to set them again in new mould and good desires. The gods are so gentle to serve, and so good to content, that if for all the services we owe them, and for the gifts which they give us, we cannot pay them in good works : they demand no more in payment but good wills. Finally I say, that if thou, Claude and Claudine, have offered the meal of youth to the world, offer now the blood of age to the gods.

I have written longer than I had thought to do. Salute all my neighbours, specially Drusio the patrician and noble Roman widow. I remember that Gobrine, your niece, did me a pleasure, the day of the feast of the mother Berecinthia, wherefore I send two thousand sesterces, one thousand to help to marry her, and the other thousand to help to relieve your poverty. My wife Faustine is sick, and I send you another thousand sesterces to give to the vestal virgins, to pray to the gods for her. My wife sendeth to thee, Claudine, a coffer, by the immortal gods I swear unto thee I cannot tell what is in it. I beseech the gods, since you are aged, to give you a good death, and to me and Faustine they suffer us to lead a good life. Marcus of Mount Celio with his own hand writeth this.

IV

That Princes and Noble Men ought to re-member that they are mortal and must die, where are sundry notable consolations against the fear of Death. [Chap. xlviii.]

¶ Cleobolus and Biton were the sons of a renowned woman, the which was Nun to the goddess Juno : and when the day of that solemn feast was celebrated, her children prepared a chariot, wherein their mother should go to the temple. For the Greeks had this custom, the day that the priests went to offer any sacrifices either they were carried on men's arms, or in chariots. They adorned their temples so well, they esteemed their sacrifices so much, and did so much honour their priests, that if any priest did set his foot on the ground, that day they did not permit him to offer any sacrifices to the gods.

It chanced as this Nun went in her chariot and her children, Cleobolus and Biton, with her, the beasts which drew the chariot suddenly fell down dead ten miles from the temple of the goddess Juno. The children, seeing the beasts dead, and that their mother could not go afoot, and that the chariot was all ready, and that there were no beasts to draw it, they (as loving children) determined to yoke themselves and draw the chariot as if they had been dumb beasts. And as the mother carried them nine months in her womb, so did they draw her in the chariot ten miles.

Now for that they passed through infinite numbers of men to the great feast of the goddess Juno, every man seeing Cleobolus and Biton yoked in the chariot like beasts, were greatly amazed, saying that these two children deserved with great rewards to be recompensed. And truly they said justly and so they deserved it. For they deserved as much to be praised for the example which they showed to all children to reverence their parents, as for carrying their mother in the chariot to the temple.

So after that the feast was ended, the mother, not knowing how to requite the benefit of her children, with many prayers besought the goddess Juno, that she with the other gods would be contented to give her two children the best thing that the gods could give to their friends. The goddess Juno answered her, that she was contented to require the other gods, and that they would do it, and the reward was, that for this noble fact [1] the gods ordained, that Cleobolus and Biton should sleep one day well, and in the morning when they should wake, they should die.

The mother pitifully bewailing the death of her children and complaining of the gods, the goddess Juno said unto her : ' Thou hast no cause why to complain, since we have given thee that thou hast demanded : and hast demanded that which we have given thee. I am a goddess, and thou art my servant, and therefore the gods have given to thy children the thing which they count most dear, which is death. For the greatest revenge which amongst us gods we can take of our enemies, is to let them live long, and the best thing that we keep for our friends, is to make them die quickly.'

¶ The author of this history is called Hisearchus in his Politics, and Cicero in his first book of his Tusculanes. In the Isle of Delphos, where the Oracle of the god Apollo

---

[1] 'fact,' feat.

was, there was a sumptuous temple, the which, for want of reparation, fell down to the ground, as often times it chanceth to high and sumptuous buildings which from time to time are not repaired. For if the walls, dungeons, castles and strong houses could speak, as well would they complain for that they do not renew them, as the old men do for that we do not cherish them.

Triphon and Agamendo were two noble personages of Greece, and counted for sage and rich men : the which went unto the temple of Apollo and built it new again, as well with the labour of their persons, as with the great expenses of their goods. When the building was achieved, the god Apollo said unto them that he remembered well their good service, wherefore he would they should demand him anything in reward of their travail, and with a good will it should be granted. For the gods use, for a little service, to give a great reward. Triphon and Agamendo answered unto the god Apollo, that for their good will, for their travail, and for their expenses, they demanded no other reward, but that it would please him to give them the best thing that might be given unto man, and that unto them were most profit : saying that the miserable men have not the power to eschew the evil nor wisdom to choose the good. The god Apollo answered, that he was contented to pay them their service which they had done, and to grant them that which they had demanded. By reason whereof Triphon and Agamendo having dined suddenly, at the gates of the temple, fell down dead. So that the reward of their travail, was to pluck them out of their misery.

The end to declare these two examples is to the end that all mortal men may know that there is nothing so good in this world as to have an end of this life : and though to lose it there be no savour, yet at the least there is profit. For we would reprove a traveller of great foolishness, if sweating by the way he would sing : and after at his journey's end he should begin to weep. Is not he simple, which is sorry for that he is come into the haven ? Is not he simple that giveth the battle, and fighteth for that he hath got the victory ? Is not he stubborn, which is in great distress, and is angry to be succoured ? Therefore, more foolish, simple, and stubborn is he which travelleth to die, and is loth to meet with death. For death is the true refuge, perfect health, the sure haven, the whole victory, the flesh without bones, fish without scales, and corn without straw. Finally, after death we have nothing to bewail, and much less to desire.

¶ In the time of Adrian, the Emperor, a philosopher called Secundus (being mar-

vellously learned) made an oration at the
funeral of a noble Roman matron (a kins-
woman of the Emperor's) who spake exceeding much evil of life, and marvellous
much good of death. And when the Emperor
demanded him what death was, the philosopher answered : ' Death is an eternal sleep,
a dissolution of the body, a terror of the rich,
a desire of the poor, a thing inheritable, a
pilgrimage uncertain, a thief of men, a kind
of sleeping, a shadow of life, a separation of
the living, a company of the dead, a resolu-
tion of all, a rest of travels, and the end of all
idle desires. Finally, death is the scourge
of all evil, and the chief reward of the good.'

¶ Truly this philosopher spake very well,
and he should not do evil which profoundly
would consider that he had spoken. Seneca
in an epistle declareth of a philosopher whose
name was Bassus, to whom when they demanded what evil a man can have in death,
since men fear it so much, he answered : ' If
any damage or fear is in him who dieth, it
is not for the fear of death : but for the vice
of him which dieth.' We may agree to that
the philosopher said, that even as the deaf
cannot judge harmony, nor the blind colours,
so likewise they cannot say evil of death, in
especially he which never tasted it. For of
all those which are dead none returned again
to complain of death : of these few that live,

all complain of life. If any of the dead returned hither to speak with the living and as they have proved it, so they would tell us. If there were any harm in secret death, it were reason to have some fear of death : but though a man that never saw, heard, felt, nor tasted death, doth speak evil of death, should we therefore fear death ? Those ought to have done some evil in their life, which do fear and speak evil of death. For in the last hour, in the straight judgment, the good shall be known and the evil discovered.

There is no prince, nor knight, rich nor poor, whole nor sick, lucky nor unlucky, which I see with their vocations to be contented, save only the dead : which in their graves are in peace and rest, and are neither covetous, proud, negligent, vain, ambitious, nor dissolute. So that the state of the dead ought to be best, since we see none therein to be evil contented.

And since, therefore, those which are poor do seek wherewith to enrich themselves, those which are sad do seek whereby to rejoice, and those which are sick do seek to be healed, why is it, that those which have such fear of death, do seek some remedy against that fear ? In this case I would say, that he which will not fear to die, let him use himself well to live. For the guiltless taketh away fear from death. The divine Plato demanded Socrates how he behaved himself in life, and how he would behave himself in death. He answered : ' I let thee wit that in youth I have travailed to live well, and in age I have studied to die well : and since my life hath been honest, I hope my death shall be joyful. And though I have had sorrow to live, I am sure I shall have no pain to die.' Truly these words were worthy of such a man.

Men of stout hearts suffer marvellously, when the sweat of their travail is not rewarded, when they are faithful, and their reward answereth nothing to their true service : when for their good services their friends become unthankful to them, when they are worthy honour and that they prefer them to honourable room and office. For the noble and valiant hearts do not esteem to lose the reward of their labour, but think much unkindness when a man doth not acknowledge their travail.

O happy are they that die : for without inconvenience and without pain every man is, in his grave. For in this tribunal, justice to all is so equally observed, that in the same place where we have deserved life, in the same place we merited death. There was never, nor never shall be, judge so just, nor in justice so upright that giveth reward by weight, and pain by measure, but sometimes they chastise the innocent and absolve the guilty, they vex the faultless, and dissemble with the culpable. For little availeth it the plaintiff to have good justice, if conscience want to the judge that should minister. Truly it is not so in death, but all ought to count themselves happy. For he which shall have good justice, shall be sure on his part to have the sentence.

When great Cato was censor in Rome, a famous Roman died, who showed at his death a marvellous courage : and when the Romans praised him for that he had so great virtue, and for the words he had spoken, Cato the Censor laughed at that they said, for that they praised him. And he being demanded the cause of his laughter, answered : ' Ye marvel at that I laugh, and I laugh at that you marvel. For the perils and travails considered wherein we live, and the safety wherein we die, I say that it is no more needful to have virtue and strength to live, than courage to die.' The author hereof is Plutarch in his Apothegms.

We cannot say but that Cato the Censor spake as a wise man, since daily we see shamefast and virtuous persons suffer hunger, cold, thirst, travail, poverty, inconvenience, sorrows, enmities, and mishaps, of the which things we were better to see the end in one day, than to suffer them every hour. For it is less evil to suffer an honest death, than to endure a miserable life. O how small consideration have men to think that they ought to die but once. Since the truth is, that the day when we are born and come into the world is the beginning of our death : and the last day is when we do cease to live. If death be no other but an ending of life, then reason persuadeth us to think that our infancy dieth, our childhood dieth, our manhood dieth, and our age shall die : whereof we may consequently conclude, that we die every year, every day, every hour and every moment. So that thinking to lead a sure life, we taste a new death.

I know not why men fear so much to die, since that from the time of their birth, they seek none other thing but death. For time never wanted to any man to die, neither I knew any man that ever failed of this way. Seneca in an epistle declareth that as a Roman woman lamented the death of a child of hers, a philosopher said unto her : ' Woman, why bewailest thou thy child ? ' She answered: 'I weep because he hath lived twenty-five years, and I would he should have lived till fifty. For amongst us mothers, we love our children so heartily, that we never cease to behold them, nor yet end to bewail them.' Then the philosopher said : ' Tell me, I pray thee, woman, why dost thou not complain of the gods, because they created not thy son many years before he was born : as well as thou complainest that they have not let him live fifty years ? Thou weepest that he is dead so soon : and thou dost not lament that he is born so late. I tell thee true, woman, that as thou dost not lament for the one, no more thou oughtest to be sorry for the other. For without the determination of the gods, we cannot shorten death : and much less lengthen life.' So Pliny said in an epistle, that the chiefest law which the gods had ͻiven to human nature was, that none should have perpetual life. For with disordinate desire to live long, we should rejoice to go out of this pain.

Two philosophers, disputing before the great Emperor Theodosius, the one said that it was good to procure death : and the other likewise said it was a necessary thing to hate life. The good Theodosius, taking him by the hand, said : ' All we mortals are so extreme in hating and loving, that under the cover to love and hate life we lead an evil life. For to suffer so many travails, for to preserve it, that sometimes it were much better to lose it.' And further he said : ' Divers vain men are come into so great follies, that for fear of death they procure to hasten death. And having consideration to this, me seemeth that we ought not greatly to love life, nor with desperation to seek death. For the strong and valiant men ought not to hate life so long as it lasteth: nor to be displeased with death when he cometh.' All commended that which Theodosius spake: as Paulus Dioconus saith in his life.

Let every man speak what he will, and let the philosophers counsel what they list, in my poor judgment, he alone shall receive death without pain, who long before is prepared to receive the same. For sudden death is not only bitter to him which tasteth it: but also it feareth him that hateth it. Lactantius said, that in such sort man ought to live, as if from hence an hour after he should die. For those men which will have death before their eyes, it is impossible that they give place to vain thoughts. In my opinion, and also by the advice of Apuleius, it is as much folly to fly from that which we cannot avoid, as to desire that we cannot attain.

And this is spoken for those that would fly the voyage of death which is necessary: and desire to come again which is impossible. Those that travel by long ways, if they want anything, they borrow it of their company. If they have forgotten ought, they return to seek it at their lodging, or else they write unto their friends a letter. But I am sorry that if we once die, they will not let us return again. We cannot speak, and they will not agree we shall write, but such as they shall find us, so shall we be judged. And that which is most fearful of all, the execution and sentence is given in one day.

Let princes and great lords believe me in this. Let them not leave that undone until after their death, which they may do during their life. And let them not trust in that they command : but in that while they live they do. Let them not trust in the works of another : but in their own good deeds. For in the end one sigh shall be more worth, than all the friends of the world. I counsel, pray, and exhort all wise and virtuous men, and also myself with them, that in such sort we live, that at the hour of death we may say we live. For we cannot say that we live, when we live not well. For all that time which without profit we shall live, shall be counted unto us for nothing.

FROM

'The fourth booke of the Diall of princes
. . . containing many instructions and rules
for the favored of the Court.'

Of the good countenance and modesty the courtier should have in behaving himself at the prince or noble man's table in the time of his meal. [Chap. vii.]

¶ Those that are abiding still in princes' courts, must in any case go seldom, or not at all, abroad to others' tables, but always to keep their own. For that courtier that runneth from table to table, to eat of others' cost, to have his meat free, is not so sparing of his purse, as he is too prodigal and lavish of his good reputation. Therefore Eschines the philosopher being demanded one day what a man should do to be counted good, he answered thus : ' To become a perfect Greek, he must go to the church willingly, and of good devotion, and to the wars of necessity : but to feasts and to banquets neither of will nor of necessity, unless it be to do them honour and pleasure that do invite thee.'

Suetonius Tranquillus writeth, that the Emperor Augustus prohibited in Rome that no man should invite each other, to feast or banquet with another, but if his friend would do him the honour to come to his feast, that then he should send him home to his house, of that meat he should have had at the feast and banquet with them at their houses. And when he was asked of certain of his friends what he meant to make this law, he gave them this answer : ' The cause that moved me, my good friends, to forbid plays and banquets in Rome was : because in play no man kept himself from swearing and terribly blaspheming the name of God : and in banquets every man is given to detect and defame his neighbour.'

Cicero recounteth of Cato the Censor, that he lying in his death bed, at the mercy of God, should say these words : ' Four things I remember I have done in my life wherein I have rather showed myself a voluptuous and negligent Barbarian, than a wise and good Roman citizen, for the which I find myself sore grieved.

¶ ' The first is, for that I spent a whole day and forgot to serve the gods, and did not profit my common weal in anything, which I should never have done. For it is as great a dishonour for a philosopher to be counted an idle and negligent person : as it is for a noble heart to be counted a rank coward.

¶ ' The second is, for that safely I might once have gone by land, and perilously I hazarded myself upon the water. A thing which well I should have let alone. For never no wise man should ever have put himself into peril, unless it were only for the service of the gods, for the increase of his honour, or for the defence of his country.

¶ 'The third is, that I opened once a great secret and matter of importance to a woman, which I ought less to have done than all the rest. For in grave matters and things of counsel, there is no woman capable to give counsel, and much less to take it, and least of all to keep it secret.

¶ 'The fourth was, that another time I was contented to be overcome by a friend of mine that earnestly invited me to his house to dinner, and thereupon I went with him, which I should not have done. For to say the truth, there was never famous nor worthy person that went to eat in another man's house but that he diminished his liberty, hazarding also his gravity and reputation to the rumour and bruit of others.'

The which words being so wisely spoken by the prudent Cato, were well worthy to be noted and carried away, and so much the more that being now drawing to his last home and even in his last breathing hour, he only spake of these four things and no more, whereof, although he were a Roman, yet he showed to us a repenting mind.

But woe is me, that albeit I bear the name

of a Christian, yea and that I am so in deed, yet in that last day when nature summons me, I fear me, and believe assuredly, I shall have cause to repent me of more than four things. Now by these things heretofore recited we may easily conjecture, that albeit we are contented to be entreated and requested in many things, yet in this only to go to others' tables to feast, and in strange houses we should not be entreated, but rather compelled and against our wills. And where the courtier is forced by importunancy to accept the bidding, without offering himself before, he deserveth as great thanks of the bidder for his coming, as the other did in bidding him. For if it should not be so, it should seem rather a dinner for strangers that travel by the way, than for noblemen and gentlemen that come from the court. For that day the courtier granteth to dine with any man, the same day he bindeth himself to be beholding to him that bids him, for although he come to him of good will, yet to acquite his courtesy done him, he is bound of necessity.

Also it is a small reputation (and worthy great reproach) that a courtier make his boast he hath eaten at all the tables and officers' boards in the court, and that no man can say he hath once been at dinner or supper with him at his own house. And truly, I remember I knew once a courtier that might dispend above two hundred ducats by the year, who told me and assured me that he never bought stick of wood to warm him within his chamber, nor pot to heat his meat in, neither spit to roast withal, nor that ever he had any cater for his provision, save only that he had made a register of many noble men's boards, amongst whom he equally divided his dinners and suppers. By means whereof he saved all his charges, save only his men's board wages.

But what vileness or discourtesy could equal the misery and shame of this careless courtier ? Sure not that of the meanest and poorest knave of the world that liveth only by his hire—no, it deserveth not to be compared unto it. For to what end desire we the goods of this world, but that by them we may be honoured, relieve our parents and kinsmen, and thereby win us also new friends ? What state or condition so ever he be of, that hath enough and abundance, we are not bound to esteem the more of him for that, nor to do him the more honour, but only for that he spendeth it well, and worshipfully, and for his honour if he be honourable. And this we speak of gentlemen as of citizens.

And he that in court makes profession to dine at other men's tables, I dare undertake if they dine betimes on the holy day, he will rather lose service in the morning than dinner at noon. And if any friend come to live with these sort of courtiers, and that he be but newly come to the court, straightway he will have him with him to dinner, and bring him to salute the gentleman where he dines that day, saying, that he was bold to bring his kinsman and friend with him to salute him, and all this is not so much to bring him acquainted with him, as it is to spare his meat at home for both.

And yet they have another knack of court finer than this. They flatter the pages and servants, because they should ever give them of the best wine at the table, and with certain familiar nods and sweet words they entertain the lords, sewers, and carvers, and make much of them that they should set before them full dishes and of the best and daintiest meat. There are also some of these courtiers that to be well waited upon at the table, and to make them his friends, do sometimes present the steward with a velvet cap, the sewers with a pair of washed or perfumed gloves, the pages with a sword girdle, and the butlers or cupboard keepers with some other pretty reward or device.

And it chanceth oft times in noble men's houses that there are so many guests to dine and sup with them daily, that many times the board will not hold them all by a great

number, which when they once perceive, to
see how quickly and with what speed the
courtiers take their places to set them down
and to be sure of a room, it is a world to see it.
But oh, I would to God they were so happy
and diligent to go to the church and hear a
sermon, as they are busy to get them stools
to sit at the table. And if, perhaps, a
courtier come late, and the table be already
full, and the lurch[1] out, yet he will not be
ashamed to eat his meat nevertheless. For
albeit he cannot be placed at his ease, yet
he is so bold and shameless that rather than
fail he will sit on half a buttock, or behind
one at the table. I remember I saw once at
a noble man's board three courtiers sit upon
one stool, like the four sons of Amon, and
when I rebuked them for it, and told them it
was a shame for them, they answered me
merrily again that they did it, not for that
there wanted stool, but to prove, if need
were, if one stool would bear the three. Such
may well be called greedy gluttons, and
shameless prowlers, without respect or
honesty, that when they are dead, would be
buried in the highest place of the church :
and when they are alive, little force at whose
table they sit, or how they sit, little regarding
their honour or estate.

[1] Lurch, a big lead in a game (O.F. *lourche*, a game akin to
backgammon). So = ' though the others be a course ahead.'

Truly for him that is poor and needy, to
seek his meat and drink where he may come
by it best, it is but meet : but for the gorgeous
courtier, bedecked with gold, bebuttoned
and bejewelled, sitting in his velvets and
silks, to beg and to seek his dinner daily at
every man's board, being nobly and honourably entertained of the prince, and able to
bear his countenance : what reproach, defame and dishonour is it to him ? He that
useth daily to run to other men's tables, is
oft times forced to sit lowest at the board
upon a broken stool, and to be served with a
rusty knife, to eat in foul dishes, and to drink
for a change hot water, and wine more than
half full of water, and to eat bare bread, and
that that of all others yet is worst of all,
every one of the servants looks over their
shoulders on him, and are angry with him
in their minds. Truly he that with these
conditions goeth abroad to seek his dinner,
were better in my opinion to fast with bread
and water at home, than to fill his belly
abroad.

But such men's reward, that haunt men's
houses in this manner, is this in the end, that
the noble men to whose houses they come
are offended with them, that stewards of the
house murmur at them, that pages and
servants mock them and laugh them to
scorn, that tasters and cup bearers chafe

with them in their minds, that cupboard keepers wonder at them, that clerks of the kitchen think them importunate and shameless creatures. Wherefore it followeth (whoever will observe it) that so soon as the servants see him once come into the dining chamber, some of them hide the stool where he would sit down, others set before him the worst meat of the board and the filthiest dishes they have, and therefore he that may have at home at his house his poor little pittance well dressed, a fair white table cloth, a bright knife, new and white bread, wood and candle in the winter, and other necessaries : if he like better to go from table to table, from kitchen to kitchen, and from one buttery to another, I will suppose he doth it for great spare and hardness, or for want of honesty and good manners.

Now he that keeps an ordinary house, and remains always at home, may dine if it be in the summer season in his shirt, if he list, he may sit when he will, and where it please him, he drinks his wine fresh, and hath the flies driven from his table with the ventola, he disdaineth the court and noble men's boards, keeping his own as frank and as sparing as he list, and no man to gainsay him : yea, and after meat he is at liberty to sit still and take his ease, or to walk abroad in the shade as he will. And in winter if perhaps he be wet, he straight shifts him, and changes all his clothes, gets him a furred nightgown on the back of him, and a pair of warm slippers to heat his cold feet withal, he eats his meat warm and smoking hot, and takes that he likes best, he drinks white wine, red wine, or claret wine as he thinks good, and need never to care for them that behold him. And therefore so great privileges as those be of liberty, the courtier should never refuse to buy them for his money, much less for the gain of a meal's meat he should leave to enjoy them.

But if the courtier will determine to visit noble men's boards, he must be very ware that in coming to a noble man's table, he do not so much commend his fare and ordinary, that he complain of other men's tables where he hath fed. For it is a kind of treason to defame and slander those whose houses they are wont to visit oft. And when he is set at the table, the courtier must behave himself modestly, he must eat temperately and finely, he must delay his wine with water, and speak but little : so that those that are present can not but praise him for his temperancy and sober diet, but also for his wisdom and moderate speech. To feed mannerly is to be understood, not to blow his nose in his napkin, nor to lean his arms upon the table, not to eat to leave nothing in the dish, not to find faults with the cooks, saying the meat is not enough, or not well dressed. For it were a great shame for the courtier to be noted of the waiters, to be a belly gut and to be counted a gross feeder.

There are some also that make themselves so familiar and homely in the house, that they are not contented with that is served them in the dish, but shamefully they pluck that to them that is left in other dishes, so that they are esteemed for jesters, no less saucy and malapert in their order, than insatiable in their beastly eating. The good courtier must also take heed he lay not his arms too far on the table, nor that he make any noise with his teeth or tongue, nor smack with his mouth when he eateth, and that he drink not with both his hands on the cup, nor cast his eyes too much upon the best dishes, that he gnaw nor tear his bread with his teeth, that he lick not his fingers, nor have done eating before others, nor to have too greedy an appetite to the meat or sauce he eats, and that in drinking he gulp not with his throat. For such manner of feeding rather becometh an ale house than a noble man's table.

And although the courtier cannot go over all the dishes that come to the board, yet at least let him prove a little of every one, and then he must praise the good cookery and fine dressing of them all. For commonly the noble men and gentlemen that invite any to their board take it uncourteously, and are ashamed if the invited praise not their meat and drink they give them, and not only the noble men are ashamed of it, but also the other officers that have the charge to see it well dressed, and in good order. Always he that eateth at another man's table, to do as he ought, should praise the worthiness of him that had him (yea though perhaps he made a lie) and commend the great care and diligence of his officers in furnishing his table with so good meats, and in setting it forth in so good order.

I say not without a cause that sometimes a praise with a lie may well stand together, since we see some noble men's tables so slender furnished, and that his ordinary should seem rather a preparative supper and diet for a sick man that means to take physic in the morning, than an ordinary or dinner for Easter day. And therefore I say, that right the lords and masters are pleased, when they hear their officers and servants commended : for they choose most commonly such a steward as they know to be wise and courteous of nature : a treasurer, true and faithful : a purveyor, expert and diligent : a butler, hasty and melancholy : the groom of his chamber, painful and trusty : his secretary, wise and secret : his chaplain simple, and his cook fine and curious. For many think it more glory to have an excellent cook in their house, than to have a valiant captain to keep a strong peace or hold. They are contented in court that noble men's chaplains be rather simple than otherwise, or well learned. For if he read but little, he hath the sooner said service, and therefore also is more fit to drudge and do service about the house.

Now therefore continuing our begun purpose, the courtier that eateth at other men's tables, must see he drink little, and that his wine be well delayed with water. For wine tempered with water bringeth two commodities : the one, it makes him sober that drinks it, and shall not be overseen : the other, he shall not distemper himself that the waiters have any occasion to laugh at him. If it should happen sometimes that he found the wine well watered before, that it had stood appalling long, or that it were somewhat sharp or sour, or that the water were too hot : the good courtier should not therefore immediately complain and find fault at the table, for so he should shame the servants, and make them angry with him, and also displease their master.

Truly it is a grief to suffer it, to see that he that hath nothing at home in his own

house, either to eat or to drink, will yet look
to be well used at another man's house, and
is never satisfied. I speak it for certain
indiscreet courtiers, and wanting judgment,
that being at any man's board (without any
shame) dare dispraise the cooks, and speak
ill of them, if perhaps the taste of their
porridge and meat mislike them, and that it
be not good, and according to their appetite :
and of the butlers, if the wine be not cold and
fresh : of those that wait above, if every-
thing they call for be not done at a beck and
quickly : of the stewards of the house, if
they be not served immediately : and of the
boys and pages, if they give them not drink
suddenly : of the carvers, if they carve
them not to their liking : and also with the
clerks of the kitchen, if they see them not
served with meat enough, that there be
enough left upon the table. So that the
noble men's officers (for the more part) have
more trouble and displeasure, by the discontentation of those that come to their
master's table, than they have by the evil
words their masters speak to them. And
for this respect, therefore, no man ought to
be so bold as once to open his lips to complain of any want in another man's house,
as if they serve him with claret wine rather
than with white : or with white than claret.
For a right and perfect courtier should not

set his appetite in the taste or variety of wines or meats in another's house.

I grant, that it is very fit and lawful for young courtiers, to run well, to leap far, to throw the bar of iron, to dance well, to ride a horse well, to manege and give him his career well, and to turn well, to handle his weapon well, and to break a staff well, and otherwise to help himself with all manner of weapons : but for one to defy another in drinking, it should be a great sacrilege of the courtier. The Scythians, as ratifieth Trogus Pompeius, were so sober and modest in eating and drinking at their meats, that it was a foul fault among them to break wind, or belch. And therefore, nowadays, we find few Scythians, but many drinkers which depart from the feast so full straight, as immediately when they come home they unload their charged stomach, and lay open all they have eaten and drunken. Wherefore he that useth to drink clean and pure water, is at more liberty than those that drink wine simply, without compound. For excessive drinking of wine, doth not only trouble and distemper the brain and judgment of the drinker : but further discovereth to you great and horrible vices.

Therefore, yet touching our matter, I say once again, that it is fond to dispute an argument, to prove which of the wines were best, pleasant, and most sweet, and which is oldest or newest, sharp or hard, soft or sweet, clearest or darkest, or of best taste or quickest savour.   For to judge of the taste of wines, and to know the goodness and perfection of it, rather (to say truly) belongeth to a taverner or vintner than rightly to an honest courtier.   And it is fitter, and more decent also for him, to talk of arms and chivalry, than to deal in discourse of Bacchus feasts.

What a mockery and foolish niceness is it of him, that not only drinks water alone, but also cannot drink it in that cup where there hath been wine filled before.   He shall also be very circumspect that is bidden to a stranger's house, that he drink not so deep at a draught that he leave nothing in the cup, neither that he drink so long as he hath breath, and the water stand in his eyes again. For the grave and sober courtier should never drink till he might no more, nor till there were none left.

And when he is at the table, he should not enter in argument or dispute with any, neither should he be obstinate in opinion, and much less use filthy or uncomely talk : and he must also bridle nature much that he cry not out in laughing as some do.   For like as it soundeth to his reproach, to be noted a glutton and drunkard, it is in like case far worse, to be accounted a fool, and a jester.

Also it prevaileth little that a courtier be moderate and honest in eating, if he be dishonest and insolent in his talk. For many times it happeneth at noble men's boards, that they take more pleasure in some than in other some: not to see them eat and drink well, but to hear them tell lies, and to be pleasant at the board.

Therefore, as we have said, the wise courtier should praise and commend all that he seeth served at another man's table, and it is not lawful for him to dislike or dispraise it. And further, because he is fed at another man's charge, he must of necessity take all in worth that is given him, and set before him, and not to look to have that that he desireth. And when there is any question moved at the table of the best and most delicate dishes, and of the finest cooks and of the new kinds of broths and sauces, and from whence the fattest capons come, it shall not be fit for the wise courtier to say in that all that he knoweth and understandeth. For how much honour it is for him to be able to talk in martial feats, or chivalry: so much more dishonour and reproach it is to him, to be skilful in dressing of meats, and all to fill the belly. I remember that being one day at a bishop's board, I heard a knight make great boast and vaunt, that he could make seven manner of fricassees, four kinds of pies, twelve sorts of sauces, and ten of fruit tarts, and twelve divers ways to dress eggs : but to hear him tell all these things was not to be accounted of so much as the gestures and countenance he made in telling them. For he did lively shew with his hands the present making of them, the eating of them, and the right tasting of them with his tongue.

And because it happeneth many times that in some noble man's house there is not like fare and entertainment that another hath, the civil courtier should not be so dishonest, as to make report he leaveth the noble man's table, to go to another's that is better served. For the worthy courtier should not haunt that table where he fareth best, but where he findeth himself best welcome and esteemed. Ah! how many noble men and knights' sons are there, that spare not to go to any man's board for his meat and drink, yea, though it fall out they be their fathers' enemies : and they do it not in respect to reconcile them and their fathers togethers, but rather for a good meal's meat, or more aptly to say, to fill their bellies with dainties.

What company the Courtier should keep and how he should apparel himself. [Chap. viii.]

¶ The wise courtier, both in court and out of court, and in all places where he cometh, must take great regard he accompany with none but with wise and virtuous men. For if he do not, he cannot win nor acquire such honour by his well doing, as he shall lose his credit by keeping ill company. And therefore he shall enforce himself always to be in the presence and company of virtuous and noble men, and shall confer with the most grave, wise, and honest gentlemen of the court. For using this way, he shall bind them to him, by reason of his daily access to them, and he shall purchase himself a good opinion of them, besides the good example he shall leave to others to tread his steps, and follow his course.

For what is more true than, when a young gentleman cometh newly to the court, you shall see immediately a company of other young fools, a company of amorous squires, light and idle persons, a company of troublesome jesters, and covetous praters, besides other young fry in court, that when they know a new come courtier (namely being of great living). They will seek to attend upon him and train him to the lure of their affects and manner, bringing him to like of their qualities and conditions. Wherefore cunningly to shake off the route of these needy, greedy retainers, he must altogether feed them with fair words, and show them good countenance and yet notwithstanding seek by all policy he can to fly their fellowship and company.

Noble men's sons, knights' sons, and gentlemen's sons, may not think their friends sendeth them to the court to learn new vices and wicked practices, but to win them new friends, and obtain the acquaintance of noble men, whose credit and estimation with the prince may honour and countenance them, and by their virtues and means, may after a time be brought into the princes' favour also, and daily to rise in credit and reputation amongst others.

Therefore such fathers as will send their children to the court, unless they do first admonish them well how they ought to behave themselves, or that they recommend them to the charge and oversight to some dear and especial friend of theirs, that will reprove them of their faults when they do amiss : I say they were better to lay irons on their feet, and send them to Bedlam or such other like house where mad men be kept. For if they be bound there in irons, it is but to bring them to their wits again, and to make them wise : but to send them to the court loose, and at liberty without guide, it is the next way to make them fools, and worse than mad men, assuring you, no greater danger or injury can be done to a young man, than to be sent to the court, and not committed to the charge of some one that should take care of him, and look straightly to him. For otherwise, it were impossible he should be there many days, but he must needs run into excess and foul disorder, by means whereof he should utterly cast himself away and heap upon his parents' heads continual curses, and griefs, during their lives.

And therefore their fathers (supposing after they have once placed their sons in the court, that they should no more cark nor care of them, nor reckon to instruct them to be wise and virtuous) find when they come home to them again, that they are laden with vices, ill complexioned, worse apparelled, their clothes all tattered and torn, having vainly and fondly spent and played away their money, and worst of all forsaken their masters, leaving them displeased with their service.

And of these I would admonish the young courtier, because he must of necessity accompany with other young men, that in no case he acquaint himself with vicious and ill-disposed persons, but with the honest, wise and courteous : amongst whom he shall put upon him a certain grave and staid modesty fitting himself only to their companies, being also apt and disposed to all honest and virtuous exercises, decent for a right gentleman and virtuous courtier, shunning with his best policy the light, foolish and vain toys of others.

And yet notwithstanding these, my intent and meaning is not to seem to persuade or teach him to become a hypocrite, but only to be courteous, honest, and well beloved of other young gentlemen: winning this reputation withal, to be esteemed for the most virtuous and honestest among them, gallant and lively in his disports and pastimes, of few words, and small conversation amongst boasters and backbiters, or other wicked and naughty persons: not to be sad among those that are merry, nor dumb among those that talk wisely, and of grave matters : nor to believe he should be accounted a trim courtier, to take his book in his hands to pray when others will take the ball to play, or go about some other honest recreation or pastime for exercise of the body. For so doing, they would rather take him for a fool and a hypocrite, than for a virtuous and honest young man : being good reason the child should use the pleasures and pastimes of a child : young men disports and acts of youth : and old men also grave and wise recreations fit for them. For in the end, do the best we can, we cannot fly the motions of the flesh, wherein we are born into this world.

These young gentlemen courtiers must take heed that they become not troublesome, importunate, nor quarrellers, that they be not filchers, liars, vagabonds, and slanderers, nor any way given to vice. As for other things, I would not seem to take from them their pastime and pleasure but that they may use them at their own pleasure. And in all other things lawful and irreprovable, observing time and hours convenient, and therewithal to accompany themselves with their fellows and companions.

Also the young courtier that cometh newly to the court, must of necessity be very well apparelled, according to his degree and calling, and his servants that follow him well appointed. For in court men regard not only the house and family he cometh of, but mark also his apparel and servants that follow him. And I mislike one thing very much, that about the court they do rather honour and reverence a man brave and sumptuous in apparel being vicious, than they do a man that is grave, wise, and virtuous. And yet nevertheless the courtier may assure himself of this, that few will esteem of him, either for that he is virtuous or nobly born, if he be not also sumptuously apparelled and well accompanied, for then only will every man account and esteem of him.

Wherefore, I durst take upon me to swear, if it were possible to take oath of our bodies, that they would swear they needed them not, much less desire so large compassed gowns, that every puff of wind might swell them as the sails of a ship, neither so long that trailing on the ground they gather dust, and cast it into our eyes. Howbeit I think now-adays these fine men wear them large and wide, and women long with trains upon the ground, because, in the court and elsewhere, no man makes reckoning of him that spendeth but orderly, and only upon necessaries to go cleanly withal, but him they set by that is prodigal, excessive and superfluous. And who that in his doings and apparel is moder-ate, and proceedeth wisely, they hold him in court for a miserable and covetous man : and contrarily he that is prodigal and lavish in expense, him they count a noble and worthy person.

Albeit the courtier come of a noble house, and that he be young of years, rich, and wealthy, yet would I like better he should use rather a certain mean and measure in his apparel (wearing that that is comely and gentlemanlike) than others of most cost and worship. For like as they would count him a fool for wearing that he could not pay for : so they likewise would think him simple, if he wear not that that become him, and that he might easily come by. His apparel should be agreeable with his years, that is to say, on the holy days some more richer and braver

than on the work days : and in the winter
of the hottest furs : in the summer light
garments of satin and damask : and to ride
with, some others of lesser price and more
durable. For as the wisdom of man is known
by his speaking : so is his discretion dis-
cerned by his apparel.

Let not the poor courtier study to wear
or devise any new or strange fashioned
garment, for if he be of that humour, he shall
quickly undo himself, and give others occasion also to follow his light and vain invention. They are nowadays found out so
many strange ways to dress meat, and so
many fashions and patterns of apparel that
now they have universities of tailors and
cooks. What more greater vanity and lightness can there be than this, that they will
not suffer the mothers' gowns to be made fit
for their daughters : saying that they are
old and out of fashion, and that they use
now a new kind of apparel and attire far
from the old manner. And notwithstanding
these gowns be it in manner new, good, whole,
clean, rich, and well made and without weme,[1]
yet their daughters must needs have new
gowns at their marriage. So that we may
aptly say that a new folly seeks always a
new gown, namely when they are light
persons, without wit and discretion.

[1] 'weme,' spot.

And I pray you, is it not a goodly sight in the court, to see a foolish courtier wear a demi-cap, scant to cover the crown of his head, to have his beard merquizotted, a pair of perfumed gloves on his hands, his shoes cut after the best fashion, a little curted cap, his hose fair pulled out, his doublet sleeves bravely cut and pinked, his rapier and his dagger gilted by his side : and then on the other side the pestilence of penny he hath in his purse to bless him with, and besides he is deep in the merchant's book for all those things he hath taken up credit of him. Their nags' foot clothes would not be so little and narrow that should seem a friar's hood, neither so great and large as the foot clothes of bishops' mules.

Also the courtier must see that his foot cloth be good and whole, clean and without spot, not tattered and seam rent. This we speak because there are some miserable courtiers that have their foot clothes thread-bare, broken and seam rent, foul and dirty, narrow, and all digged full of holes with spurs.

And therefore no man deserveth to be called a right courtier, unless he be fine and neat in his apparel he weareth, and also courteous and civil in his words and entertainment.

And yet touching the rest of the furniture

of their horse, or gelding, their harness and traps must be kept black and clean, and they must look that the reins of the bridle be not broken nor unsewed, which I speak not without cause : for there are a number of courtiers that at primero will not stick to set up a jest of a hundred or two hundred crowns and yet will think much to give their poor horse keepers twelve pence to buy them a pair of reins. And truly the courtier (in my judgment) that is content to tie his hose with untagged points, to see his fire smoke when he should warm him, to ride with broken reins, and to cut his meat at the table with a rusty knife, I would think him base born, and rudely brought up.

When the courtier will ride his horse, let him look ever before he take his back that he have all his furniture fit for him, his mane and tail finely combed, his stirrups bright glittering, his stirrup leathers strong, and his saddle well stuffed, and, above all, let him sit upright in his seat, and carry his body even, swerving of neither side, holding his legs still and keeping his stirrup. For this name to be called Chevalier (signifieth in our tongue a rider of a horse) came first because he could ride and manege his horse well. And when he would stir his legs to spur his horse, let him beware he stoop not forward with his body, and when he doth spur his horse, let him not spur him low, but high in the flanks, and whether he will run or stand still with his horse, let him always have his eye upon the reins, and in no case the reins go out of his hand.   And in giving his horse a career, let him not writhe his body, nor be too busy in beating or spurring his horse oft.   For in his career, to know when to spur him, when to give him head or to pull him back again and to stop him, I have seen many take it upon them but few indeed that ever were skilful and could do it well.

Now the courtier being mounted on horse or mule, without his rapier by his side, seemeth rather a physician that goeth to visit his sick patients, than a gentleman of the court that for his pleasure and disport rideth abroad through the streets.   And if he were by chance entreated by some noble man to accompany him, or to ride behind him of pleasure through the streets, every honest courtier ought not only to do it, but unasked to be ready to offer himself to wait upon him and go with him willingly.

And let the fine courtier beware that in giving his hand to a gentlewoman he be not gloved, and if she be ahorseback that he talk with her bareheaded, to do her more honour, and if she ride behind him and they chance to discourse together, let him never look back upon her to behold her, for that is

a rude manner and a token of ill education.
And one common courtesy there is among
courtiers, that when they are in talk with
ladies and gentlewomen and entertaining of
them, they suffer them to do with them what
they will, to reign over them and to be overcome in argument of them, and they hold it
good manner to do them service, when they
have any occasion offered to serve them.
And when he shall accompany any gentlewoman to go a visitation with her, or to talk
abroad for their pleasure through the streets,
he must ride fair and softly, and if she should
happen to keep him so long in talk till she
should light, the good courtier must bear it
courteously, and make a good countenance
as though it grieved him nothing, since we
know very well, that when women begin once
to talk, it is impossible for them to make an
end, unless they be overtaken with night, or
prevented by some other accident.

He that will be a courtier, must wear his
shoes black and clean, his hose straight to
his legs, and his garments without plight or
wrinkle, his sword fair varnished, his shirts
finely wrought, and his cap standing with a
good grace. For the chiefest thing of court
is, that noble men be rich in apparel, and the
right courtiers fine and cleanly. It is not
decent for a man to wear his slippers so long
that the cork be seen, nor his garments till

they be torn, nor fur till it be bare before, nor
shirts till they be worn out, nor his cap till
the truss be greasy, nor his coat till it be
threadbare, nor his girdle till it be half broken.
For the courtier may not only wear his garments to content himself, but also to like
others that shall behold it. And after that
he is once determined to go to the court, he
must suppose to go thither well apparelled,
otherwise they will not account him to be a
right courtier. For in this case, excuse of
poverty may not be alleged, for they will
think them rather miserable,[1] than poor
courtiers. The good courtier may not spare
in court, to spend afterwards at home : but
he must pinch at home to be liberal afterwards in the court.

And yet once again I return to recite, that
for a courtier to come into the prince's favour,
he may not any way be sparing or miserable,
but rather honestly liberal and bountiful.
For seldom times concur these two things
together, to be miserable and yet with his
misery to attain to the prince's favour. I
remember I saw a friend of mine once in the
court wear a jerkin faced at the collar with
martens and they were all bare and greasy,
and there was a certain portingall [2] in the
court (a pleasant companion) that came to
this gentleman and asked him properly, what

---

[1] 'miserable,' miserly.   [2] 'portingall,' Portuguese.

fair furs they were he wore about his neck, and this gentleman answered him 'Martens.' 'Martens, Sir,' saith the portingall, 'methinks they are rather like furs of Ash Wednesday, than of Shrove Tuesday.' And finely this portingall compared Mardi (that is Tuesday) to his marten furs : and so likewise his marten furs to Mardi. And sure he had great reason not to praise them, but greatly to rebuke him for them. For it had been more for his honour and worship, to have had the collar of his jerkin lined with fair new white lamb, than with so old, stale, dirty and sweaty martens.

The brooches that our courtier must wear in his cap must be very rich, and excellently wrought, and his device or word that he will have about it such that though every man may read it, yet few shall understand what it means. For such devices are ever lightly grounded of vain and fond toys, and therefore they should be so much more secret and obscure. For surely the fault is great enough in a man to devise it, though he do not bewray it.

Also his servants that wait upon him must needs go handsomely apparelled, and fine and neat in their apparel, for it is small honour for the master to be well apparelled, if he let his servants go beggarly. There are many courtiers that have their men following on them with threadbare cloaks, torn coats, foul shirts, broken hose, and rent shoes : so that these poor serving men, if for one month they wear that their master giveth them, for three other months after they wear their own proper flesh. It is no wise man's part, but a mere folly to keep a greater train than he is able. For that courtier that hath always many servants waiting on him, and they going tattered and torn, having no good thing to put on their backs (or at least that they have is but mean and simple), shall sooner win the name of a broker, that preferreth other men to service, than of a master that keepeth servants himself.

The good courtier must give unto all his servants that serve him, either apparel, or wages : for that servant that serveth only in house for bare meat and drink, shall never serve truly while he doth serve. And therefore let the courtier look well to it, that he entertain no man into his service, but that first he agree with him for standing wages, unless it be that he be some nephew or kinsman or some of his dear friends : else in the end, if he be a noble man (unless he do so) he shall find that at the year's end he shall spend him more, than if he gave him ordinary wages, and besides they will not be contented with him, although it be to his greater charge.

Also let him consider well if it happen that (when he hath need of servants to wait upon him) some brother or neighbour's child be offered to him, whether he shall receive him or no. For after he hath him in his house, either he shall be compelled to bear with his faults, and disorders he shall do, or else desirous to rebuke and reform him, or to send him home again, he shall but win anger and displeasure of his father or his proper kinsfolk. Surely such courtiers as take those kind of men into their service have a great deal of pain and trouble with them. And truly it is too great a cruelty, that the courtier should be driven to bear the dishonesty of his man that serves him, when his own father could not away with his conditions. Some fathers there are so blinded and sotted with fatherly affection, and difficult besides to please, that they are not contented that the courtier hath received their son into his service, and that he entreat him as if he were his own kinsman : but further they would have the courtier, his master, bear with all his dishonesty and lewdness : and if they cannot frame the young man to their mind as they would have them, yet at least they would have his master to pity him, for that he is but young and hath no knowledge, and for a while to wink at his faults, in hope of a better amendment.

The courtier may not only see that his men be well in apparel, but he must provide also that they have meat enough to put in their bellies. For the servants that are starved for meat, are wont to do small service, and besides that, to complain much.

Let him beware also he do not take into his service any lewd persons, busybodies and unquiet men, cutpurses, ruffians, quarrellers or whoremongers : if he find that he hath any such in his house, let him turn them out of service straight : for by keeping such mates in his house, his house shall never be well ordered, there shall ever be quarrelling and swearing amongst them, and besides that, the neighbours and common people shall be offended.

Let the good courtier foresee that he hath no cards nor dice in his house to occupy the servants. For these thriftless servants that are given to play, begin first to play, and afterwards they learn to steal.

Let the courtier be well advised also when he chideth his servants, that he be not too loud, that his voice may be heard abroad, as all the hosts' and innkeepers' are. For in being too loud he should be more dishonoured, than blamed for the ill words he giveth his man. Let him take heed also that he do not call his servants drunkards, thieves, villains, Jews nor other suchlike names of reproach. For these and such other like uncourteous words are of small correction, and yet they bring displeasure and disdain enough.

And if the courtier cannot give bountifully, and pleasure his officers and servants that are about him, yet at least (howsoever the world go) let him not be behind with them in paying them their whole wages due to them : for so it might lightly happen that the servants would begin to make complaints of him, and that unhappily, in the end, he might come to die with misery in his enemies' hands. There is no enemy in the world so cruel, nor so much to be feared, as the servant that is not contented with his master, for as he is the thief of the house, so knoweth he very well what piece of his master's harness is wanting for his body to set on him, when he would in that place have an arrow for his token. Therefore so soon as it cometh to the courtier's ears that any of his servants complain of him, either let him give him all that he would have, or put him out of his house immediately. For if he do it not, let him be assured that the servant will never leave till he have put him in discord with his friends, and defame with others.

And above all things we have spoken of yet, the courtier must chiefly look what his man is he trusteth with his honour : for in this case many are wont not only to be deceived, but also many times scorned. And there are many that will put their goods into the hands and trust of a man, but their honour and things of greatest weight and importance, they will sooner commit to the trust of a young, foolish, and simple page than of a wise and staid man. And therefore how much more his business is of weight and importance, so much less should it be revealed to the secrecy of a boy. And if he do otherwise, I can assure him he shall sooner be spoken of of every man, than he shall have his business despatched.

The courtier must also have his chamber well hanged, and finely kept, and clean, and his house and family all in good order, and every man quiet. For the cleanness of the house and civility of the servants, are a great token and witness of the nobility of the master. In the courtier's chamber where he lieth, the bed must first of all be made, and the cloth before the door let down, the chamber swept, the hangings and other stuff that is there in good order, with some perfumes or other sweet odours, so that it should laugh upon a man that comes into it : for there are some in the court so filthy and so ill furnished of hangings and other stuff that, if any man come to see their chambers, they seem rather sheepcotes than courtiers' chambers.

FINIS

APPENDIX A

From RELOX DE PRINCIPES, Bk. II. chap. xiv.
(1537 fol.)

DICHO como el empador Marco aurelio tenia el estudio en lo mas apartado de su palacio : y como el mismo tenia la llave de aql estudio : es de saber agora q jamas a muger ni a hijos ni a familiares amigos deraua entrar dẽtro : porq̃ muchas vezes dezia el. Co mas alegre coraço sufrire q me tomen los thesoros que no que me rebueluan los libros. Acotecio que un dia la emperatriz faustina estando preñada importuno con todas las maneras de importunidad q̃ pudo tuuiesse por bien de darle la llave de el estudio y esto no es maravilla : porque naturalmente las mugères menosprecian lo que les dan y mueren por lo que les niegan. Insistia faustina en su demada : y esto no de burla sino de veras no una vez sino muchas non con solas palabras sino con palabras y lagrimas diziendole estas razones. Muchas vezes te he rogado me diesses la llave de tu camara y tu siempre los has echado en burla y no los deurias, senor mio hazer acordandote que estoy prenada : porque muchas vezes los maridos lo que oy echan en burlas manana lo lloran de veras. Acordarte deurias que soy yo Faustina la muy nombrada la qual en tus ojos soy la mas hermosa en tu lengua la mas alabada de tu persona la mas regalada de tu coraçon la mas quista : pues si es verdad que me tienes en tus entranas : por

R

que dudas de mostrarme tus escrituras ? Comunicas comigo los secretos del imperio : y ascondes de mi los libros de tu estudio ? Has me dado tu coraçon tierno : y niégas me agora la llave que es de hierro duro ?

The same: From Berthault's Lorloge des Princes (1550 ed.)

Nous avons dit commêt l'empereur Marc Aurele tenoit son estude au plus secret lieu de son palais et comme luy mesmes en gardoit la clef, a sçavoir est, que jamais n'y laissoit entrer femme ny enfans, ny aucun de ses amys familliers : car il disoit souvent, de meilleur cœur souffriray que lon me prenne mes tresors, que non que lon me trouve mes livres. Il advint qu'un jour l'imperatrice Faustine, estant enceincte importuna l'impereur, par toutes les manieres qu'elle peut, qu'il voulsist estre tant gracieux envers elle, qu'il lui donnait la clef de son estude. Et ce n'est de merveilles, pour ce que naturellement les femmes mesprisent ce que lon leur donne, et meurent apres la chose que lon leur nye, Faustine insistoit en sa demande non une fois, mais plusieurs, non seulement de parolles mais avecques abondantes larmes, luy disant ces raisons : Je t'ay par plusieurs fois prié, que me donnasses ou voulsisses bailler la clef de ta chambre, et tu la m'as toujours refusee pour mocquerie : ce que tu ne devrois faire, rememorant que je fus enceincte, pource que les maris prennent jeu aujourd'huy ilz le pleurent l'endendemain. Tu te devrois recorder que je suis Faustine celle tât renommee, laquelle en tes yeulx suis la plus belle, et en ta langue la plus louee, et de ta personne la plus aymee, et de ton cœur la mieulx requise. Doncques s'il est vray que tu me tiens en tes entrailles, pourquoy doutes tu a me monstrer tes escritures. Tu communicques avecques moy les secretz de l'empire, et tu caches de moy les livres de ton estude. Tu m'as donné ton tendre cœur, et tu me nyes maintenant la clef qui est de fer si dur.

APPENDIX B

The following is a specimen passage from Berners' GOLDEN BOKE, (1538(9) edition), chap. xxxi. (fol. 52) :

What a vilayne sayde to the senatours of Rome in the presence of the emperour.

This emperour, beyng sicke, as it is aforesayd, on a daye, as there were with hym divers physitions and oratours, there was a purpose moved amonge theym, how greatly Rome was chaunged, not all onely in edifyces, but also in customes, and was full of flatterers, and unpeopled of men that durste say the trouthe. Than the emperour sayd : The fyrste yere, that I was consull, there came a poore vilayne from the ryver of Danubie, to aske justyce of the senate, agenst a censure, who dydde dyvers extortions to the people : and he hadde a small face and great lippes, and hollowe eyes, his heare curled, bareheeded, his shoes of a porkepes skyn his coat of gotis heare, his gyrdell of bulle rushes and a wild eglantyne in his hand. It was a strage thing to se hym so monstruous and mervayle, to here his purpose. Certaynly, whan I saw hym com into the senate, I wende it had bene some beaste, in the figure of a manne. And after I had harde hym, I judged him one of the goddes, yf there be goddes amonge men. And as the custome in the senate was, that the complayntes of the poore persons were harde before the requestes of the ryche : this vilayne had lycence to speake, and soo beganne his purpose wherein he shewed hym selfe as bolde in wordes, as extreme and base in his aray, and sayd : O ye auncyent fathers, and happy people, I Myles, dwellyinge in a cytie on the ryver of Danubie, doo salute you senatours, that are here assembled in the sacred senate. The dedes do permytte, and the gods suffre, that the capitayns of Rome, with theyr great pryde have reduced under subjection, the unhappy people of Germany. Great is the glory of you Romayns for your battayles that ye have wonne throughout all the worlde. But if wryters saye true, more greater shalbe your infamy, in tyme to come, for the cruelties that ye have done to the innocentes.

APPENDIX C

The following is a specimen of Bryan's DISPRAISE OF THE LIFE OF A COURTIER :

The V Chapiter

¶ *That the rusticall lyfe is more quiet and restfull and more beneficial than that of the court.*

The village whereof we speake and the demaines thereof, Put we the case that it were all free and not subject to any Lord (as certain there be so privileged) that every man there lyveth in his owne house, whether it be by succession, or that he have bought it freely without doying any homage or service to any man. This I dare say, the courtier hath not nor is not in such free libertie in respecte of such as be of the village, for as much as of very necessitie, my maister the courtier must win the Marshall or Harbengar of the lodging, and must receive at his handes the billet to come to his lodging, and that late ynough and wery to his host, breake open doors, beat downe walles, disorder houses, burne implements, and some tyme beat the good man, and defyle the wife. O how happy is he that hath wherwithal to live in the village without troubling both of himself and many sondry places, without seeking of so many lodgings, without assayes of so many straunge occasions of strange men, without weeping of any person, but is content with a meane estate, and is delivered of all such breake braines. Another benefite of the countrey is this, that the gentleman or burges that these doth inhabite may be one of the chief or chiefest, either in bountie, honor, or aucthoritie, the which happeneth seldome in the court and in great cities and townes for there he shall see other goe before him, more trim and more brave and gorgeous than he, as well in the house as without the house.

APPENDIX D

The following is an extract from Geoffrey Fenton's
GOLDEN EPISTLES (1577 4°):

A Discourse of the Ages of Man's Life.

There hath bene an auncient question, what be
the ages of mans life, and whether there be sixe or
seven of them, wherein (the better to be resolved)
we must presuppose, that this worde (Age) is under-
standed in two sortes, as the age of the worlde, and
the age of man. The age of the worlde beares
number and reckoning both according to the Poets,
and collection of the Christian authors. The Poets
make four ages of the world, the first of gold, the
second of silver, the third of brasse, and the fourth
of iron. The first inventor of this partition of ages,
was SIBYL of *Cuma* from whom the Latine Poets
drawe their conjectures, as appeareth in Ovid in the
first booke of his Metamorphosis, where he dis-
courseth upon the foure ages, when and how they
passed. And according to the accompt of the
Christians, there be eyghte ages, that is to say,
seven afore the comming of Christ, and one since.
But bycause our question concernes nothing the
ages of the world, we will leave them at libertie, and
reason only of the ages of mê : whereof I see not
how it is possible to speake resolutely, for that it
is a thing not certaine in it selfe, and hangs altogether upon the authoritie and opinions of auncient
writers, of whom we have to beleeve best, such as
we beare most credite to.

First it is affirmed by many that there be these

seven ages in the life of man, INFANCIE, PUERILITIE, MANS ESTATE, YOUTH, GRAVITIE, OLDE-AGE and STATE DECREPITE : they restraine one part of these ages to a certaine number of yeares, and leave the rest without limite. . . .

Printed by T. and A. CONSTABLE, Printers to His Majesty
at the Edinburgh University Press

Philip Allan & Co.

Foolscap 8vo.   5s. net each.

The Pilgrim's Books

EDITED BY

A GRADUATE OF CAMBRIDGE

A Series of Books to slip in the pocket when going on a walking or bicycling tour, or on a country ramble. Pleasant and cheerful, light and humorous, being for the most part choice selections from classic writers.

No. 1. THE PLEASURES OF SOLITUDE: wherein are portrayed the delights of occasional retirement. By Dr. JOHN ZIMMERMAN of Berne. A new version, by A GRADUATE OF CAMBRIDGE.

No. 2. (*In Preparation.*) TOASTS, RAKES, AND CITS. By Sir RICHARD STEELE and others.

VOLUMES IN CONTEMPLATION:

The Right Way of Living. By LUIGI CORNARO, LESSIUS, and others.

Good Thoughts in Bad Times. By THOMAS FULLER.

Selections from Addison.

The Garden of Cyrus.   And Others.

Quality Court, London, W.C. 2

Philip Allan & Co.

Demy 8vo.   10s. 6d. net.

Moments of Genius

By ARTHUR LYNCH

A brilliant and fascinating book.   The Author snapshots, as it were, certain of the world's greatest geniuses at vital moments of their careers.   Each pen-picture (there are 20 in all) represents many years of study, but the result is expressed with deft, rapid, and beautiful strokes, giving a clearer conception of character than most full-length biographies.

Crown 8vo.   With an Illustration.   10s. 6d.

The Book-Hunter at Home

By P. B. M. ALLAN, M.A.

An arm-chair book for all book-lovers.   Talks upon libraries old and new, romance ancient and modern, rare books and common books, big books and small books, thick books and thin books, good books—but not bad books.   In short it deals with a host of those matters so dear to all book-lovers.

Quality Court, London, W.C. 2

Passages to be Noted

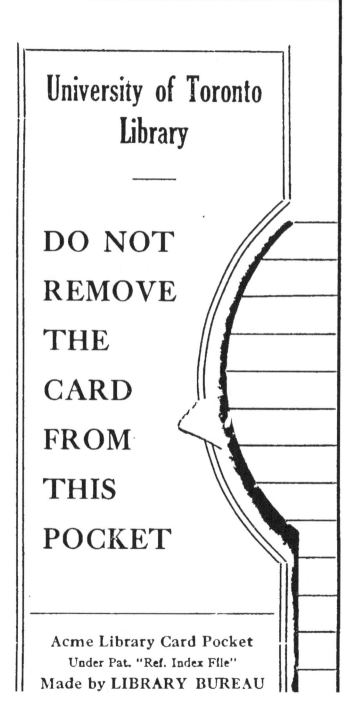

University of Toronto
Library

—

DO NOT

REMOVE

THE

CARD

FROM

THIS

POCKET

Acme Library Card Pocket
Under Pat. "Ref. Index File"
Made by LIBRARY BUREAU

Made in the USA
Middletown, DE
20 May 2019